THE MUSIC OF
MALCOLM ARNOLD

A Catalogue

Arnold as conductor, rehearsing for the London première of his Symphony No. 1 (1951).

THE MUSIC OF
MALCOLM ARNOLD
A Catalogue

COMPILED BY ALAN POULTON

FABER MUSIC
IN ASSOCIATION WITH
FABER AND FABER
LONDON AND BOSTON

First published in 1986 by Faber Music Ltd
in association with Faber & Faber Ltd
3 Queen Square London WC1N 3AU
Design and typography by James Butler
Music examples drawn by Lincoln Castle Music
Typesetting by Goodfellow & Egan, Cambridge
Cover design by M & S Tucker
Typesetting by Goodfellow & Egan, Cambridge
Printed in Great Britain by The Thetford Press

British Library Cataloguing in Publication Data

Poulton, Alan
Malcolm Arnold.
1. Arnold, Malcolm, 1921- —Bibliography
I. Title
016.78′092′4   ML134.A7/

ISBN 0-571-10057-0

CONTENTS

ACKNOWLEDGEMENTS

First, to Malcolm Arnold, my warmest thanks for the help and guidance he gave me during the compilation of this catalogue – his patience in answering a long series of questions and the accuracy of his recall are to be both appreciated and admired. Thanks are also due to Martin Kingsbury of Faber Music, publishers of Dr Arnold's music for the last two decades, for having masterminded the publication of this book.

Among the many who have also provided much-appreciated help and assistance I must mention Richard Adeney, Isobel Arnold, Leslie Avenell (Lengnick), Chris Barstow (Faber Music), James Blades, Jill Burrows, Piers Burton-Page (BBC), E. J. B. Catto (National Youth Brass Band of Scotland), Stewart Craggs, Hugo Cole, Nicola Constable (Faber Music), Carol Cooper (Old Vic), Martin Cotton (BBC Television), Timothy Day (National Sound Archive), James Diack (Paterson), Michael Dobson, Judith Donington, Denis Egan (London Coliseum), Julian Elloway (formerly Faber Music), Lt.-Col. George Evans (Royal Military School of Music, Kneller Hall), Garry Evenden, Francesca Franchi (Royal Opera House), Allan Fry (London Philharmonic Orchestra), Leon Goossens, Eileen Hall, Leslie Halliwell (whose *Film Guide*, 3rd edition, has proved to be an invaluable source of reference on Arnold's film music), John Hassell, Anthony Hodges (Royal Northern College of Music), Annetta Hoffnung, Raymond Howorth, Eric Hughes (National Sound Archive), Cynthia Hudes (Hong Kong Philharmonic Orchestra), Robin Johnson (Dartington Hall Trust), Katherine King, Beresford King-Smith (City of Birmingham Symphony Orchestra), Roderick Lakin (Society for the Promotion of New Music), Derek Lewis (BBC), Eileen Lown (who typed the first draft of the catalogue), Barrie Macdonald (IBA), Miriam Miller (BBC), Anatole Mines, Dorothy Morrison, Jacqueline Noltingk (LPO), Elizabeth Ormiston (Sunshine Fund), Pat Perilli (British Film Institute

Library Service), Brian Priestman, Guy Protheroe (formerly BBC), Kenneth Roberton, John F. Ross (National Youth Orchestra), Rachel Stockdale (British Library), Pamela Thompson (Royal College of Music), Tom Tillery (Royal Operal House), Jeremy Tyndall (Cheltenham Festival), Thomas Vaughan, David Vidgen (Performing Right Society), John Watson (EMI) and Roger Wright (British Music Information Centre).

ALAN POULTON

ILLUSTRATIONS

FOREWORD
SIR CHARLES GROVES

Two of my best friends, orchestral musicians, were close friends of Malcolm Arnold in his days as principal trumpet of the London Philharmonic Orchestra. They have told me of his quicksilver imagination and of the effortless bravura of his technique. Another colleague remembered with admiration the sound that he produced for the single trumpet note in the last chord of 'Morning' from Grieg's *Peer Gynt* music.

He has become one of the most prolific of twentieth-century composers, mining immense riches from the seam that contains Berlioz, Wagner and Richard Strauss, and transforming them by his own alchemy into a particularly striking and individual orchestral style.

Malcolm Arnold's great misfortune is that he has been too often described merely as a brilliant manipulator of the orchestra, facile and lacking in depth. I offer one example to refute that argument: the slow movement of his Second Symphony, an elegy of tragic power superbly sustained. This symphony was dedicated to myself and the then Bournemouth Municipal Orchestra at its Diamond Jubilee in 1953 when I first met Malcolm and we began a friendship that has lasted for more than thirty years.

Among contemporary composers Arnold is one of the few who have never compromised their style or methods, and when musical history catches up with our times, his music will be remembered.

I therefore welcome this timely and invaluable catalogue, which will prove of great value to the many admirers of this versatile and much-loved composer.

MALCOLM ARNOLD: AN APPRECIATION
HUGO COLE

Success, and particularly early success, brings penalties as well as rewards in its train. For over thirty years, Malcolm Arnold has been among the three or four most-played British composers, his music known to thousands through concert performances, to hundreds of thousands (many of whom may never have heard his name) through the film scores. It is built into the brains and fingers of innumerable amateurs who continually play his works. The danger is that a reputation established so early, and so firmly, will set hard and in immutable shape. Arnold is often hailed as the playboy of the Western musical world, the solitary joker allowed in every pack. In England, such a description carries with it a certain stigma; success as an entertainer seems automatically to disqualify a composer from the sort of earnest and sustained attention generously given to many 'serious' composers far less gifted and versatile than Arnold.

He himself has done something to widen the rift between himself and the musical *élite*. In interviews and broadcasts he has been openly sceptical about the activities and pretensions of the new-music establishment. Behind this stance lie attitudes and allegiances formed in his early years as an orchestral player that have tended to set him apart from the composing fraternity. He retains much of the orchestral musician's suspicion of 'paper music', of innovation for its own sake. More significantly, he was able, in his years as a player, to pass freely between many musical worlds, taking in his stride pop, jazz, light music and television jingles alongside symphonies and concertos, and shedding in the process any prejudice he might have had against commercial entertainment music.

He is not, of course, the only composer to have seen merit in types of music commonly disdained by 'serious' musicians. But it is hard to think of any other major British composer who has used the idioms of popular music so unselfconsciously, without a hint of caricature or parody, often allowing 'commonplace' tunes their own obvious harmonies or repetitive accompaniments, welcoming them into major works on equal terms with more sophisticated material.

Many of Arnold's works were purpose-built, and can be sensibly discussed only in their proper context. For occasions that demand the musical equivalent of stage scenery he has often supplied what is needed and no more. Film composers working under great pressure necessarily rely on the conventions and routines they have established for themselves, and some of Arnold's occasional concert works seem to have been dashed off just as quickly as any of the film scores. But the stimulus of writing for Julian Bream, Osian Ellis or Richard Adeney, or for such comparatively little-understood instruments as guitar and harp, produced extended works of great individuality. The limitations of a special commission, too, have often spurred him into producing outstanding works. The *Toy Symphony*, the *Grand, Grand Overture* with its obbligato parts for vacuum cleaners, floor-polisher and rifles, the Concerto for Harmonica, the Duo for Two Cellos written to fill a double spread in a teaching book and designed for students of modest attainments, are full of the genuine Arnold character and demonstrate his special flair for making the most of a musical situation that allows little room for manoeuvre.

Arnold is far from being an unsophisticated or blinkered composer. You will find bitonal passages, tone-rows and many unusual and surprising forms of motivic manipulation in his music if you look for them. But he runs counter to the spirit of the age in his refusal to tease or mystify the listener, and in his uninhibited use of repetition to drive the message home. His music can be 'difficult', or at any rate disconcerting, not by reason of unfamiliar idioms, elliptical or condensed processes or the complexity of simultaneous happenings, but as a result of his boldness, even recklessness, in bringing together elements conventionally regarded as unmixable. This applies both to his material, which within a single movement can range from the most 'popular' to the most rarified, and to his constructional techniques: sometimes blatantly obvious, at others ingeniously calculated; while the mixing of the lyrical, the macabre and the uproarious with clichés borrowed from popular music, often breaches the accepted conventions of concert-hall etiquette.

Those who expect Arnold's music to be all sunshine may also be disconcerted by the sombre mood of some of the later works. Here the message is not always clearly articulated, and it may be as ambiguous as it is in the late works of Shostakovitch. But the broadening of the emotional spectrum is significant. Often in these later works, particularly in the symphonies, he admits the existence of darkness and disruption, of negative forces, which thrust their way into the foreground. (Often the conflicts that ensue go unresolved.) And though it would be hard to trace a parallel technical evolution—an evolution of harmonic or melodic idiom—in the series of eight symphonies, written between 1951 and 1978, they remain essential listening for all who are interested in Arnold, and who would like to view his music in true perspective.

Over 40 years, Arnold's style has undergone no abrupt or disconcerting changes of direction. His music is still, predominantly, tonal, tuneful, traditional in the use of regular metres and in the handling of instruments and voices, both individually and collectively. But despite working within self-imposed limits, he has nonetheless continued to extend his technical and emotional range. A short, selective survey of works from different periods will give some idea of the persistence and ingenuity of this extension, and of the variety of techniques employed.

Early works reveal his liking for spare textures, clear tone-colours, third-based harmony and relatively simple discords. The overture *Beckus the Dandipratt*, composed in 1943, can be heard as a personal declaration of independence. There is no trace of student immaturity or pretentiousness, of academic influence, or of violent revolt against academic influence. Ribald and sometimes disquieting, it is the work of one who steers his course with certainty and knows exactly what his material is good for. There are, of course, reminiscences. The sound of the orchestra, and particularly of Berlioz's orchestra, is in his ears. Arnold's development section is apparently based on a Sibelian device, projecting melodic fragments against a side-drum roll (rather than Sibelius's characteristic string tremolos). But the influences have been so thoroughly absorbed that we would never have remarked on them if Arnold had not given us the hint.

Sibelian influence is more easily discerned in the First Symphony (completed in 1949 though not performed till 1951): in its use of homophonic brass in dramatic gestures; in its long melodic flights for solo woodwind; in the many passages for paired woodwind; in the throwing back and forth of short melodic fragments; in its powerful motivic use of the interval of a fourth; and in the way material is developed. The opening provides a textbook example of a tiny thematic cell serving as a storehouse for later developments (ex. 1). The end of the

Ex.1   Symphony no. 1 op. 22, I

reprinted by kind permission of the publishers,
Alfred Lengnick & Co Ltd

work is satisfyingly conclusive; the opening fugue subject of the last movement is first transformed into a lively march, finally appearing *maestoso* over a ground-bass of primitive simplicity, itself derived from the subject.

In the First Symphony, Arnold proved his ability to work on a large scale, sacrificing something of his own individuality as a melodist in the process. A like preoccupation with motivic development shapes many works of the forties and fifties in which Arnold's increasing professional expertise impresses, while something of the early spontaneity seems to be lacking. The energetic and rhetorical theme of the second movement of the Clarinet Concerto (1948) was clearly born to undergo musical adventures, and fulfils its role (ex. 2). But while the music is fluent and

Ex.2   Concerto for Clarinet and Strings op. 20, II

reprinted by kind permission of the publishers,
Alfred Lengnick & Co Ltd

resourceful, the special Arnold character emerges only in a few freer, quasi-improvisatorial flights for solo clarinet, and in one catchy first-movement tune that is never fully assimilated into the music.

At the same time, a parallel line of development can be traced in the genial, tuneful entertainment works, including the Three Shanties for Wind Quintet, the Serenade for Small Orchestra and the English Dances. In the Second Symphony (1952) the two Arnolds become one, and there is a harmonious and satisfying fusion of styles. Textures are spare, harmonies pure and luminous, the instrumentation as characteristic and individual as the themes themselves. There are many ingenuities if we care to look for them (such as the evolution of a principal theme of the scherzo from the horn chords of the first two bars), but the main impression on the listener is one of easy and spontaneous movement, and of inventive powers so fertile that problems are solved almost before they arise.

Arnold's tunes have a way of fixing themselves firmly in the memory, never to be dislodged. Like characters in a Dickens novel, they tend to assert their individuality in the same terms on every appearance. Arnold often shows a respect for their integrity that prevents him from manipulating or fragmenting them in ways that might destroy their identities. Instead, he will arrange for his theme-characters to appear against different backgrounds or in different contrapuntal company, or will introduce episodes which remove us from their sphere of influence, devise surprising entrances and exits for them, or involve them in canonic encounters which generally demonstrate their refusal to surrender any particle of their own identities.

This reluctance of Arnold's more memorable tunes to be anything but themselves is often a critical factor in determining both the form and the psychological effect of major symphonic movements. The big tune of the first movement of the Fourth Symphony (ex. 3) stands out in high relief not only because of its pop music connections (a cultural dissonance deliberately introduced) but because eleven repetitions of the main figure or its inversion imprint it so firmly on the listener's consciousness that all other interests become subsidiary.

The self-containedness of a 'big tune' operates in another way in the slow movement of the Fifth Symphony, which opens with a powerfully expressive melodic sentence (ex. 4) that would not be out of place in one

Ex.3   Symphony no. 4 op. 71, I

reprinted by kind permission of the publishers,
Paterson's Publications Ltd

Ex.4   Symphony no. 5 op. 74, II

reprinted by kind permission of the publishers,
Paterson's Publications Ltd

of Mahler's late *adagios*. When this theme, apparently so full of possibilities
for expansion and development, returns in just the same form at the end
of the movement, and again at the climax of the last movement, we
experience an odd sense of *déja-vu*. Commenting on this movement and
(presumably) this theme, Arnold has said that 'in time of great emotion
we speak in emotional clichés'; and certainly, the literal repetition ensures
both that the message is driven well home and that the phrase itself
appears more clichéd than it might have if varied or expanded. Perhaps
inescapable obsession is the very effect Arnold is aiming for; but it is also
possible that he is shunning the sort of developments which such ultra-
expressive themes seem to demand because they would lead him into
uncharted emotional territory.

Though much of the music gives an impression of having been freely
and spontaneously written, there is plenty of internal evidence that
Arnold moulds his material consciously and artfully. Some of the earliest
concert works, including the First Violin Sonata, the Viola Sonata and
the First String Quartet, are rich in contrapuntal device, and experiment
freely in many modes of construction. In the latter part of his career he
has increasingly experimented with themes that are in one sense or
another 'contrived', and with calculated transformation processes, often
of his own devising. Thus, in the Fifth Symphony, the main theme of the
first movement turns back on itself midway and ends with the notes of
the motto theme from the opening bars (ex. 5). The persistent bass figure
of the scherzo repeats the motto notes; the unusual harmonies in bars 5–8
of the first movement are created by running a series of two–note chords
(derived from the eight-note row shown in ex.5) in harness with its own
retrogrades (ex. 6).

Ex.5   Symphony no. 5 op. 74, I

reprinted by kind permission of the publishers,
Paterson's Publications Ltd

Ex.6   Symphony no. 5 op. 74, I

reprinted by kind permission of the publishers,
Paterson's Publications Ltd

A similar device appears in the last movement of the Second String Quartet, where the violins set up an ostinato that could be described as a retrograde canon based on a nine-note row (ex. 7). In the Concerto for 28 Players, a theme in F minor sprouts a twelve-note 'tail' that is later treated in four-part canon and combined with its own augmentation, while another nine-note row gives rise to a six-note canon at a single beat's distance.

Ex.7   String Quartet no.2 op. 118, IV

Where Arnold derives inspiration from popular or folk music, he respects the integrity of his originals; he will never refine or sophisticate as though to make popular material acceptable for polite concert-hall use. As a result, there are long passages in his music where the harmony remains static; many dance-inspired themes in particular stick as firmly to their home keys as their prototypes in the worlds of popular or functional music. Tunes which modulate, or which slip in and out of distant keys Prokofiev-wise, are, however, fairly common, and Arnold will often adapt his favourite passacaglia form so that themes, or bass-lines, modulate on each repetition (as in the Concerto for Harmonica, the Piano Trio and the Philharmonic Concerto).

He is a fluent contrapuntist, and skilled in the rare art of writing rapid orchestral counterpoint that is always bright and clear. Even tunes that sound innocently spontaneous may turn out to have considerable contrapuntal potential. The main theme of the second movement of the Sixth Symphony (in which Arnold pays tribute 'to a style of pop music

Ex.8   Symphony no. 6 op. 95, II

which will be forgotten by the time the symphony is played') is happily devised to go into canon with itself – a trick, perhaps learnt from Berlioz, by which a theme can be made to appear in a new light without losing its identity (ex. 8). He is fully aware, however, that contrapuntal writing can degenerate into a sort of musical knitting. In the major fugues he avoids this by basing each one on a specific constructional 'idea': thus, in the finale of the Fourth Symphony, the fugue subject is repeatedly broken into by an abrupt brass interjection that later forms an ostinato against which the main theme is heard, uninterrupted, for the last time (ex. 9).

Ex. 9   Symphony no. 4 op. 71, IV

reprinted by kind permission of the publishers, Paterson's Publications Ltd

In many of the less extended works, tune and treatment belong so closely together that both seem to spring from a single act of invention. The slow movement of the Concerto for Harmonica opens directly with a theme that itself dictates the movement's shape as it is passed back and forth between soloist, horns, trumpets and trombones, giving rise to new counter-themes and falling a semitone at each entry, until the final trumpet statement restores the original D minor tonality (ex. 10). In the

Ex.10 Concerto for Harmonica and Orchestra op. 46, II

reprinted by kind permission of the publishers,
Paterson's Publications Ltd

last movement of the Toy Symphony, it is hard to account for the effect produced by the unassuming little tune until we take account of the whole context: divided violas chugging along far below; toy instruments making, in all seriousness, their limited contribution, like the village bassoon in Beethoven's 'Pastoral' Symphony; those shocking, refreshing excursions to and from a remote C sharp minor. Arnold's success as a composer of occasional works is due as much to his ability to place tunes in the right context – to discern exactly what they are good for – as to the prodigality of his melodic invention.

We tend to talk about music in terms of motives, harmonic contrasts, and so on, because these are the elements that can be easily identified and analysed. Detective work that uncovers twelve-tone rows and retrograde canons is enjoyable for its own sake, but the main reason for discussing these things in Arnold's case – where such techniques are not central to the compositional process – is to indicate how much forethought and conscious planning go into the work of a composer often talked of as though he was a purely instinctive worker, a child of nature. If a precise and practicable terminology existed, it would surely be more rewarding to discuss the music in terms of textures, colours, types of articulation, or even, more broadly, in terms of the kinds of audience the composer aims to reach. In Arnold's case, we should also take into account a certain fellow-feeling with his performers that is closely reflected in his scoring. He does not require instrumentalists to play passages which look impressive on paper but make little effect in the concert hall, to expose themselves dangerously by attempting the near-impossible, or to behave in ways that would damage their instruments – or their self-respect. Most of his more original effects are produced without resort to extremes. If he rarely writes very fast music in extreme keys, it is partly because he knows the sound will be cleaner and brighter in the home keys. His refusal to use irregular rhythms and bar-lengths reflects his dislike of the extravagances of some of his contemporaries, as well as a willingness to accept restrictions as a stimulus to invention: if one can get along without setting $\frac{15}{8}$ against $\frac{9}{17}$, so much the better for all. It is remarkable how often such a brilliant and original orchestrator can be observed to be playing safe, rarely entrusting double basses with a *legato* theme on their own or sending bassoons into the heights. Bar an occasional well-prepared and supported ascent to extreme notes for horns or trumpets, Arnold generally ensures that all solos lie comfortably within the instruments' most expressive range.

Arnold has rejoiced in his ability to communicate with a wide, non-specialist audience. Music, he once said, is a social act of communication, a gesture of friendship, the strongest there is. But it has long been evident that there is a darker side to his character, even though the temptation to dredge the subconscious and to expose his own innermost feelings has not often been indulged. Disruptive forces are at work in the early 'comedy overture' *Beckus the Dandipratt*, whose main themes suffer every kind of violent assault. In later works, dark clouds will settle on a previously sunlit landscape (as in the song-like slow movement of the Second Clarinet Concerto). The sombre and threatening slow movement of the *Symphony for Brass*, with its dramatic unisons, takes us into a very different world from that of the cheerful scherzo which precedes it or the busy fugal finale.

Ex.11 String Quartet no. 2 op. 118, II

Arnold will often make bold use of picturesque dissonance, as in a striking passage from the Second String Quartet in which a ferocious ostinato in a remote key is superimposed on a simple dance tune for first violin (ex. 11). Note how the effect is enhanced by delay – we are given time to savour the tune's innocence before the lower strings break in. At other times interesting harmonic complications may result from the strict pursuit of some contrapuntal process. On occasion, deliberate disruption seems to be aimed at, as in the Seventh Symphony, where the melodic flow is twice interrupted in a manner almost brutal, in passages as 'anti-musical' as the opening *Presto* of the last movement of Beethoven's Ninth Symphony. In the finale of Arnold's Seventh, we are told by a programme note, 'destructive forces are conquered by reason'; but 'reason' is oddly represented by a tinkling sort of 18th-century tune that brings little comfort, while the last bleak cowbell notes which (again according to the composer's notes) stand for 'hope', are anything but reassuring. In the *Peterloo* overture, Ivesian havoc is let loose – appropriately enough, no doubt, in this particular piece of programme music. But if there are messages of despair in these works, they are not clearly articulated; Arnold seems to acknowledge the existence of the darker side of the human psyche, but deliberately refrains from exploring it in greater depth or detail.

It could be that the cheerful exuberance of so much of Arnold's music is partly defensive; a bold facing-out of life-denying forces, an expression of his determination not to give an inch of ground in the struggle against them. If so, perhaps we shouldn't try to penetrate those defences. Certainly, the last thing I would suggest is that we should waste time and energy in searching out inner meanings in music that is generally so self-sufficient, so much to be enjoyed for its own sake. But until we take account of the complexities of Malcolm Arnold's musical character, we will not be well-equipped to measure his full stature as a composer.

COMPILER'S PREFACE AND LIST OF ABBREVIATIONS

The Catalogue of Works attempts to list all of Malcolm Arnold's music, both published and unpublished. The sequence is chronological, but I have separated the composer's considerable output of music for film, radio, television and theatre from that for the concert hall, opera house and ballet. Information (where available) on each concert and stage work has been assembled in the following sequence: title, opus number, duration, word source(s), instrumentation*, tempo marking(s), completion date of score, location of autograph manuscript, details of first performance (artists, venue and date), details of other 'first' performances (e.g. London, British, European, broadcast) where appropriate, and details of publication. In the case of opera, ballet, film and incidental music, additional information, such as producer, director and soundtrack credits, has been added. Unless otherwise indicated, all scores are in ink.

The catalogue numbers allocated to each work are also shown in the *Classified List*, the *Chronology* and the *Discography*, where they appear in bold type.

The *Discography* is in alphabetical order for ease of reference, the *Classified List* is alphabetical within sections, and the *Bibliography* is chronological within sections.

* Numerical abbreviations in the form of, say, 2 2 2 2 – 4 3 3 1 indicate 2 flutes, 2 oboes, 2 clarinets, 2 bassoons, 4 horns, 3 trumpets, 3 trombones and 1 tuba.

The following abbreviations have been used:

a	alto	arr	arranged/arrangement
acl	alto clarinet	asax	alto saxophone
alt	alternative	b	bass

bar	baritone	ob	oboe
barsax	baritone saxophone	org	organ
bbar	bass-baritone	perc	percussion
bcl	bass clarinet	picc	piccolo
bd	bass drum	pno	piano
blra	bell lyra	rec	recorder
bnjo	banjo	s	soprano
bong	bongos	sax	saxophone
bsn	bassoon	sd	side drum
btrb	bass trombone	str	strings
ca	cor anglais	strqt	string quartet
cbsn	contrabassoon	susp-cym	suspended cymbal
cel	celesta	t	tenor
chms	chimes	tamb	tambourine
cl	clarinet	timp	timpani
cnt	cornet	tpt	trumpet
cym	cymbals	trb	trombone
db	double bass	trgl	triangle
dulc	dulcimer	trs	translation/translated by
euph	euphonium	tsax	tenor saxophone
exc	excerpt	t-t	tam-tam
fl	flute	ttrb	tenor trombone
glsp	glockenspiel	tub-bells	tubular bells
gtr	guitar	va	viola
harm	harmonica	vc	violoncello
hn	horn	vib	vibraphone
hp	harp	vn	violin
mrcs	maracas	wdbl	woodblocks
mrmb	marimba	ww	woodwind
ms	mezzo-soprano	xyl	xylophone

CHRONOLOGY

Year of Composition	Opus Number	Title and Catalogue Number
1945	12	Symphonic Suite for Orchestra **24**
1945		Prelude for Piano Solo **25**
1946	13	Symphony for Strings **26**
1946	14	Festival Overture **27**
1947	15	Sonata No. 1 for Violin and Piano **28**
1947	16	Children's Suite for Piano **29**
1947	17	Sonata for Viola and Piano **30**
1947	18	Two Bagatelles for Piano Solo **31**
1947		Avalanche Patrol **166**
1947		Seven RAF Flashes **167**
1948		Charting the Seas **168**
1948	19	Sonatina for Flute and Piano **32**
1948		Only a little box of soldiers, arr **303**
1948		To Youth **33**; *see* Little Suite No. 1, op. 53 **73**
1948		Two RAF Flashes **169**
1948	20	Concerto for Clarinet and Strings **34**
1948		Gates of Power (alt: Stairway to the Sea) **170**
1948		Hydrography **171**
1948		Report on Steel **172**
1948	21	The Smoke **35**
1948		Badger's Green **173**
1948		Mining Review **174**
1948		Metropolitan Water Board **175**
1948		Hawick, Queen of the Border **176**
1948		Women in Our Time **177**
1948		Cotton – Lancashire's Time for Adventure **178**
1948		The Struggle for Oil **179**
1949		EVWs **180**
1949		This Farming Business **181**
1949		Britannia Mews (US: The Forbidden Street) **182**
1949	22	Symphony No. 1 **36**
1949		The Frazers of Cabot Cove (alt: An Island Story) **183**
1949		Drums for a Holiday **184**
1949		Terra Incognita **185**

Year of Composition	Opus Number	Title and Catalogue Number
1951		Men and Machines **208**
1951	34	The Dancing Master **50**
1951		Wings of Danger **209**
1951		Local Newspapers **210**
1951		Home at Seven (US: Murder on Monday) **211**
1952	35	Two Ceremonial Psalms for Treble Voices **51**
1952		Stolen Face **212**
1952		The Holly and the Ivy **213**
1952		The Sound Barrier (US: Breaking the Sound Barrier) **214**
1952	36	Eight Children's Pieces for Piano **52**
1952		Channel Islands **215**
1952		The Island (alt: Kent Oil Refinery) **216**
1952		Curtain Up **217**
1952	37	Divertimento for Wind Trio **53**
1952		The Ringer (alt: Gaunt Stranger) **218**
1952	38	The Sound Barrier **54**
1952		It Started in Paradise **219**
1952	39	Concerto for Oboe and Strings **55**
1952		Four-Sided Triangle **220**
1952		Invitation to the Dance **221**
1953		Gilbert and Sullivan **222**
1953	40	Symphony No. 2 **56**
1953	41	Sonatina for Recorder and Piano **57**
1953		Katherine, Walking and Running **58**
1953	42	Homage to the Queen **59**
1953	42a	Homage to the Queen Ballet Suite **60**
1953	42b	Homage to the Queen (piano suite) **61**
1953		Tango in D (from Albéniz: España) arr **304**
1953		Purple Dust **284**
1953		The Captain's Paradise (alt: Paradise) **223**
1953		Man of Africa (alt: Kigusi Story) **224**
1953		Copenhagen, City of Towers **225**
1953		Albert RN (alt: Spare Man; US: Break to Freedom) **226**

Year of Composition	Opus Number	Title and Catalogue Number
1956	54	Piano Trio **74**
1956	55	Song of Praise **75**
1956		Port Afrique **245**
1956		Fanfare (ABC Television title music) **290**
1956		Trapeze **246**
1956		A Hill in Korea (US: Hell in Korea) **247**
1956		Wicked As They Come (US: Portrait in Smoke) **248**
1956		Solitaire **76**
1956		Fanfare for a Royal Occasion **77**
1956	56	The Open Window **78**
1956		The Barretts of Wimpole Street **249**
1956		Tiger in the Smoke **250**
1956	57	A Grand, Grand Overture **79**
1956		Roses Tattoo **251**
1956	58	Concerto No. 2 for Horn and Strings **80**
1957	59	Four Scottish Dances **81**
1957		Island in the Sun **252**
1957	60	HRH The Duke of Cambridge **82**
1957	61	Oboe Quartet **83**
1957		For Mr Pye an Island **291**
1957		Blue Murder at St Trinian's **253**
1957	62	Toy Symphony **84**
1957		The Bridge on the River Kwai **254**
1957	63	Symphony No. 3 **85**
1957		Royal Prologue **292**
1957		Dunkirk **255**
1957	64	Commonwealth Christmas Overture **86**
1957		Richmond **87**
1958		The Key **256**
1958	65	Sinfonietta No. 2 **88**
1958		Concert Piece for Percussion **89**
1958		The Roots of Heaven **257**
1958		The Inn of the Sixth Happiness **258**
1958		United Nations **90**

Year of Composition	Opus Number	Title and Catalogue Number
1958		Coupe des Alpes **259**
1959		Music For You **293**
1959		The Boy and the Bridge **260**
1959	66	Five William Blake Songs **91**
1959		On the brow of Richmond Hill (Purcell), arr **305**
1959		Four Pieces for Chamber Ensemble **92**
1959	67	Concerto for Guitar and Chamber Orchestra **93**
1959		Kingston Fanfare **94**
1959	68	Sweeney Todd **95**
1959	68a	Sweeney Todd Concert Suite for Orchestra **96**
1959		Solomon and Sheba **261**
1959		Suddenly Last Summer **262**
1959	69	Song of Simeon **97**
1959		The Pilgrim Caravan **98**
1960		The Angry Silence **263**
1960		Parasol **294**
1960	70	March: Overseas **99**
1960		Tunes of Glory **264**
1960	71	Symphony No. 4 **100**
1960		The Pure Hell of St Trinian's **265**
1960	72	Carnival of Animals **101**
1960		No Love for Johnnie **266**
1960		A Hoffnung Fanfare **102**
1960		Christmas Carols, arr **306**
1961	73	Quintet for Brass **103**
1961	74	Symphony No. 5 **104**
1961		Whistle Down the Wind **267**
1961		On the Fiddle (US: Operation Snafu) **268**
1961	75	Divertimento No. 2 **105**
1961	76	Grand Concerto Gastronomique **106**
1961		Leonora No. 4 (Beethoven – Strasser) **107**
1962		The Inspector (US: Lisa) **269**
1962		The Lion **270**
1962	77	Concerto for Two Violins and String Orchestra **108**

Year of Composition	Opus Number	Title and Catalogue Number
1967	94	The Padstow Lifeboat **127**
1967		North Sea Strike **279**
1967	95	Symphony No. 6 **128**
1967	96	Trevelyan Suite **129**
1967		This Christmas Night **130**
1967		Thomas Merritt: Coronation March, arr **308**
1968	98	A Salute to Thomas Merritt **131**
1968		Thomas Merritt: Anthems and Carols, arr **309**
1968		The First Lady **299**
1968	97	Peterloo **132**
1968	99	Anniversary Overture **133**
1968		St Endellion Ringers **134**
1969	100	Fantasy for Trumpet **135**
1969	101	Fantasy for Trombone **136**
1969	102	Fantasy for Tuba **137**
1969	103	The Song of Accounting Periods **138**
1969		The Reckoning (alt: A Matter of Honour) **280**
1969		The Battle of Britain **281**
1969	104	Concerto for 2 Pianos (3 Hands) and Orchestra **139**
1969		David Copperfield **282**
1970	105	Concerto for 28 Players **140**
1970		Fanfare for Louis **141**
1970	106	Fantasy for Audience and Orchestra **142**
1970	107	Fantasy for Guitar **143**
1971	108	Concerto for Viola and Chamber Orchestra **144**
1971		William Walton: Sonata for String Orchestra, arr **310**
1971		Popular Birthday **145**
1972	109	Song of Freedom **146**
1972	110	The Fair Field **147**
1972	111	Concerto No. 2 for Flute and Orchestra **148**
1973	112	A Flourish for Orchestra **149**
1973	113	Symphony No. 7 **150**
1973	114[a]	Fantasy for Brass Band **151**

Year of Composition	Opus Number	Title and Catalogue Number
1973	114[b]	Two John Donne songs **152**
1974	115	Concerto No. 2 for Clarinet and Orchestra **153**
1975	116	Fantasy on a Theme of John Field for Piano and Orchestra **154**
1975		Railway Fanfare **155**
1975	117	Fantasy for Harp **156**
1975	118	String Quartet No. 2 **157**
1976		The Three Musketeers **158**
1976	119	The Return of Odysseus **159**
1976	120	Philharmonic Concerto **160**
1977	121	Sonata for Flute and Piano **161**
1977	122	Variations for Orchestra on a Theme of Ruth Gipps **162**
1977		Hard Times **300**
1978	123	Symphony for Brass Instruments **163**
1979	124	Symphony No. 8 **164**
1980		The Wildcats of St Trinian's **283**
1981	125	Concerto for Trumpet and Orchestra **165**

CLASSIFIED LIST OF WORKS

SOLO PIANO

CHAMBER

Eight English Dances (Set 2), op. 33, piano–duet arr **49a**
Fantasy for Bassoon, op. 86 **118**
Fantasy for Clarinet, op. 87 **119**
Fantasy for Flute, op. 89 **121**
Fantasy for Guitar, op. 107 **143**
Fantasy for Harp, op. 117 **156**
Fantasy for Horn, op. 88 **120**
Fantasy for Oboe, op. 90 **122**
Fantasy for Trombone, op. 101 **136**
Fantasy for Trumpet, op. 100 **135**
Fantasy for Tuba, op. 102 **137**
Five Pieces for Violin and Piano, op. 84 **115**
Four Pieces for Chamber Ensemble (1959) **92**
Katherine, Walking and Running (1953) **58**
Oboe Quartet, op. 61 **83**
Phantasy for String Quartet (1941) **8**
Piano Trio, op. 54 **74**
Popular Birthday, reduced version (1972) **145a**
Quintet for Brass, op. 73 **103**
Quintet for Flute, Violin, Viola, Horn and Bassoon, op. 7 **19**
Sonata for Flute and Piano (1942) **12**
Sonata for Flute and Piano, op. 121 **161**
Sonata for Viola and Piano, op. 17 **30**
Sonata No. 1 for Violin and Piano, op. 15 **28**
Sonata No. 2 for Violin and Piano, op. 43 **62**
Sonatina for Clarinet and Piano, op. 29 **45**
Sonatina for Flute and Piano, op. 19 **32**
Sonatina for Oboe and Piano, op. 28 **43**
Sonatina for Recorder and Piano, op. 41 **57**
String Quartet No. 1, op. 23 **37**
String Quartet No. 2, op. 118 **157**
Symphony for Brass Instruments, op. 123 **163**
Three Shanties for Wind Quintet, op. 4 **16**
Trevelyan Suite, op. 96 **129**
Trio for Flute, Viola and Bassoon, op. 6 **18**
Wind Quintet, op. 2 **13**

CONCERTOS

Concerto for 2 Pianos (3 hands) and Orchestra, op. 104   **139**
   version for 2 pianos (4 hands) and orchestra (Elloway)   **139a**
Concerto for Clarinet and Strings, op. 20   **34**
Concerto for Flute and Strings, op. 45   **64**
Concerto for Guitar and Chamber Orchestra, op. 67   **93**
Concerto for Harmonica and Orchestra, op. 46   **65**
Concerto for Oboe and Strings, op. 39   **55**
Concerto for Organ and Orchestra, op. 47   **66**
Concerto for Piano Duet and Strings, op. 32   **48**
Concerto for Trumpet and Orchestra, op. 125   **165**
Concerto for Two Violins and String Orchestra, op. 77   **108**
Concerto for Viola and Chamber Orchestra, op. 108   **144**
Concerto No. 1 for Horn and Orchestra, op. 11   **23**
Concerto No. 2 for Clarinet and Orchestra, op. 115   **153**
Concerto No. 2 for Flute and Orchestra, op. 111   **148**
Concerto No. 2 for Horn and Strings, op. 58   **80**
Fantasy on a Theme of John Field for Piano and Orchestra, op. 116   **154**
Grand Concerto Gastronomique, op. 76   **106**
Philharmonic Concerto, op. 120   **160**
Serenade for Guitar and Strings, op. 50   **69**

ORCHESTRAL

Anniversary Overture, op. 99   **133**
Beckus the Dandipratt, op. 5   **17**
Carnival of Animals, op. 72   **101**
Commonwealth Christmas Overture, op. 64   **86**
Concerto for 28 Players, op. 105   **140**
Divertimento No. 1 for Orchestra, op. 1   **11**
Divertimento No. 2, op. 24   **39**
Divertimento No. 2, op. 75   **105**
English Dances (Set 1), op. 27   **42**
English Dances (Set 2), op. 33   **49**
The Fair Field, op. 110   **147**

Tam O'Shanter, op. 51   **70**
Theme and Variation (1966) (from *Severn Bridge Variations on a
    Welsh Folk Song*)   **124**
To Youth (1948)   **33**
Toy Symphony, op. 62   **84**
United Nations (1958)   **90**
Variations for Orchestra on a Theme of Ruth Gipps, op. 122   **162**
Water Music, arr, op. 82b   **113a**

BRASS BAND

Fantasy for Brass Band, op. 114[a]   **151**
Four Cornish Dances, op. 91, arr (Farr)   **123b**
Four Scottish Dances, op. 59, arr (Farr)   **81a**
Little Suite No. 1 for Brass Band, op. 80   **112**
Little Suite No. 2 for Brass Band, op. 93   **126**
The Padstow Lifeboat, op. 94   **127**

CEREMONIAL

Fanfare for a Festival (1955)   **71**
Fanfare for a Royal Occasion (1956)   **77**
Fanfare for Louis (1970)   **141**
Flourish for a 21st Birthday, op. 44   **63**
A Hoffnung Fanfare (1960)   **102**
Kingston Fanfare (1959)   **94**
Railway Fanfare (1975)   **155**
Richmond (1957)   **87**

MILITARY BAND

Homage to the Queen Ballet Suite, op. 42a (Finale only), arr
    (Dunn)   **60a**
HRH The Duke of Cambridge, op. 60   **82**

Little Suite No. 1, op. 53, (March only), arr (Sumner)   **73a**
Little Suite No. 2 for Brass Band, op. 93, arr
    (Singerling)   **126a**
March: Overseas, op. 70   **99**
The Padstow Lifeboat, op. 94, arr (Woodfield)   **127a**
The River Kwai March (1957), arr (Vinter)   **254**

CONCERT AND SYMPHONIC BAND

English Dances (Set 1), op. 27, arr (Johnstone)   **42b**
Four Cornish Dances, op. 91, arr (Marciniak)   **123a**
A Grand, Grand Overture, op. 57, arr (Wilson)   **79a**
'Prelude', 'Siciliano' and 'Rondo' from Little Suite No. 1 for Brass Band,
    op. 80, arr (Paynter)   **112a**
'Sarabande' and 'Polka' from Solitaire (1955), arr (Paynter)   **76b**
Water Music, op. 82   **113**

SOLO VOCAL

Five William Blake Songs, op. 66   **91**
Kensington Gardens (1938)   **5**
The Peacock in the Zoo (1963)   **110**
The Song of Accounting Periods, op. 103   **138**
Two John Donne Songs, op. 114[b]   **152**
Two Songs for Voice and Piano, op. 8   **20**

CHORAL (ACCOMPANIED)

John Clare Cantata, op. 52   **72**
Jolly Old Friar (1966)   **125**
'The Pilgrim Caravan' from Song of Simeon, op. 69   **98**
Psalm 150: Laudate Dominum, op. 25   **40**
The Return of Odysseus, op. 119   **159**
Song of Freedom, op. 109   **146**

RVW 1st noel
Oh Xmas night.

CHORAL (UNACCOMPANIED)

OPERA

BALLET

MUSICALS/REVUES

FILMS: FEATURE

FILMS: DOCUMENTARY

INCIDENTAL: TELEVISION

INCIDENTAL: RADIO

INCIDENTAL: THEATRE

Purple Dust **284**
The Tempest **285**

ARRANGEMENTS OF MUSIC BY OTHER COMPOSERS

Christmas Carols, arr soloists and various combinations **306**
Double-Hoquet (Machaut), arr brass trio **302**
Motet – Marie assumptio (Anon, 13th century), arr brass trio **301**
Only a little box of soldiers (music-hall song), arr voice and pno **303**
On the brow of Richmond Hill (Purcell), arr a and str **305**
Tango in D (Albéniz: España, op. 165 no. 2), arr orchestra **304**
Thomas Merritt: Anthems and Carols, arr satb chorus and various combinations **309**
Thomas Merritt: Coronation March, arr brass band **308**
William Walton: Sonata for String Orchestra, arr of String Quartet, last movement only **310**
We Three Kings of Orient Are, arr pno and orchestra **307**

CATALOGUE
OF WORKS

CONCERT AND STAGE WORKS

1936

1 HAILE SELASSIE   duration unknown
March for piano solo
Score completed   *c*August 1936
Autograph MS   untraced

The manuscript was sent to Boosey & Hawkes but returned by them on
8 September 1936 with the standard rejection letter.

1937

2 ALLEGRO IN E MINOR FOR PIANO SOLO   0′40″
Score completed   13 February 1937
Autograph MS   pencil score, held by the Royal College of Music,
     London

3 THREE PIANO PIECES   2′45″
I   *Prelude*: Moderato
II   *Air*: Andante cantabile
III   *Gigue*: Allegro vivace
Score completed   15 February 1937
Autograph MS   pencil score, held by the Royal College of Music,
     London

4 SERENADE IN G FOR PIANO SOLO   1′30″
Andante
Score completed   3 October 1937
Autograph MS   inscribed 'To Mother, love from Malcolm', held by the
     Royal College of Music, London

1938

5 KENSINGTON GARDENS 7'30"
Song-cycle for medium voice and piano
Text: Humbert Wolfe
I *Night*: Andante con moto (18 July)
II *Tulip*: Allegro moderato (28 April–12 June)
III *Noon*: Andante con moto (24 July)
IV *Daffodil*: Andante con moto (24 April–12 June)
V *Lupin*: Allegretto (27 April)
VI *Hawthorn Tree*: Andante (24 May)
VII *The Rose*: Presto – Allegretto – Presto – Adagio (May)
VIII *Laburnum*: Andante moderato (12 May)
IX *The Chestnut and the Beech Tree*: Allegretto (May)
Score completed 24 July 1938
Autograph MS ink and pencil score, held by the Royal College of
Music, London

6 DAY DREAMS 2'45"
for piano solo
Allegro moderato
Score completed 3 October 1938
Autograph MS inscribed 'Many Happy Returns of the Day, with love
from Malcolm', held by the Royal College of Music, London

1939

7 TWO PART-SONGS 1'45"
Texts: Ernest Dowson
I *Spleen*: Andante con moto
II *Vitae Summa Brevis Spem Nos Uetat Incohare Longam* [no tempo
marking]
Score completed 24 September 1939
Autograph MS held by the Royal College of Music, London

1941

8   PHANTASY FOR STRING QUARTET   12'00"
Andante con moto – Andante – Presto – Andante con moto – Andante –
   Molto presto
Score completed   London, 17 June 1941
Autograph MS   score and parts, held by the Royal College of Music,
   London

This work, originally entitled 'Vita Abundans', was placed second in the
W. W. Cobbett prize for composition in 1941. The *Presto* section was
later incorporated into the Wind Quintet, op.2, and other sections into
a projected first symphony (distinct from Arnold's first published
symphony); the score of Phantasy for String Quartet has a number of
markings in red pencil to indicate instrumentation (flute, clarinets,
trumpets, etc.).

9   TWO PIANO PIECES   2'00"
I   Quickly
II   Allegro moderato con molto espressivo
Score completed   3 October 1941
Autograph MS   inscribed 'with love to Mother from Malcolm', held by
   the Royal College of Music, London

1942

10 PIANO SONATA IN B MINOR   9'00"
I   Allegro ma non troppo
II   Andante con moto
III   Alla marcia
Score completed   Cornwall, August 1942
Autograph MS   inscribed 'With love to Mother from Malcolm,
   Christmas, 1942', held by Roberton Publications
First performance   Richard Deering, British Music Information Centre,
   London, 15 May 1984

First broadcast performance   Richard Deering, BBC World Service,
   3 August 1984
Publication   Roberton, 1984

1   DIVERTIMENTO NO. 1 FOR ORCHESTRA   Opus 1   10'30"
   3 2 2 2 – 4 3 3 1 – timp 2perc – str
   I   Moderato – Vivace
   II   Andante con moto (Chaconne) – Allegro
   Score completed   London, date unknown
   Autograph MS   untraced
   First performance   London Symphony Orchestra/Benjamin Frankel,
      Guildhall School of Music, London, 29 May 1945 (Committee for the
      Promotion of New Music concert)

2   SONATA FOR FLUTE AND PIANO   8'30"
   I   Andante con moto – Allegro [alternating tempi]
   II   Recitative – Allegro
   III   Allegro
   Score completed   12 November 1942
   Autograph MS   held by the Royal College of Music, London

   The Sonata for Flute and Piano was an early experiment in serial
   technique.

3   WIND QUINTET   Opus 2   13'00"
   fl ob cl hn bsn
   I   Allegro
   II   Presto
   III   Alla marcia
   Score completed   London, date unknown
   Autograph MS   untraced
   First performance   London Philharmonic Orchestra Wind Quintet:
      Richard Adeney (fl), Michael Dobson (ob), John Lucas (cl), Charles
      Gregory (hn), George Alexandra (bsn), Trinity College of Music,
      London, 7 June 1943 (Committee for the Promotion of New Music
      concert)

The London Philharmonic Orchestra during Arnold's time as principal trumpet, in rehearsal for the 1942 season of Promenade Concerts (Arnold is in the extreme left of the picture, below the timpani).

With Denis Egan, playing slide trumpets formerly belonging to the English trumpeter Thomas Harper (1786–1853), now held by the Royal College of Music, London (1946).

1943

14 THREE PIANO PIECES   7'00"
I   *Prelude*: Andante lamentoso
II   *Romance*: Andante con molto espressivo
III   *Lament*: Andante moderato
Score completed   London, 6 May 1943
Autograph MSS   two copies, one inscribed 'Many Happy Returns, with
    love to Mother from Malcolm, October 3rd 1944', held by the Royal
    College of Music, London

15 LARCH TREES Opus 3   8'30"
Tone poem for orchestra
2 2 2 2 – 4 0 0 0 – str
Andante con moto
Score completed   London, 20 June 1943
Autograph MS   score and parts held by the Royal College of Music,
    London
First performance   London Philharmonic Orchestra/Malcolm Arnold,
    Royal Albert Hall, London, 1 October 1943 (Committee for the
    Promotion of New Music concert)
First broadcast performance   Northern Sinfonia/Christopher Seaman,
    BBC Radio 3, 7 December 1984
Publication   Faber Music, 1985

16 THREE SHANTIES FOR WIND QUINTET Opus 4   6'30"
fl ob cl hn bsn
I   Allegro con brio – Presto
II   Allegro semplice
III   Allegro vivace
Score completed   London, date unknown
Autograph MS   untraced
First performance   London Philharmonic Orchestra Wind Quintet, Filton
    Aerodrome, Bristol (in an aircraft hangar, during a lunchtime shift),
    cAugust 1943
Publication   Paterson, 1952, and Carl Fischer, 1967

BECKUS THE DANDIPRATT   Opus 5   8'30"
Overture for orchestra
2+picc 2 2 2 – 4 2+cnt 3 1 – timp perc – str
Allegro ma non troppo
Score completed   Capel Garmon, Llanrwst, date unknown
Autograph MS   untraced
First broadcast performance   BBC Scottish Orchestra/Ian Whyte, BBC
   Third Programme, 29 November 1946
First concert performance   London Philharmonic Orchestra/Eduard van
   Beinum, Royal Opera House, Covent Garden, London, 16 November
   1947
First American performance   University of Illinois Symphony
   Orchestra/Rafael Kubelik, University Auditorium, Illinois, 29 March
   1952
Publication   Lengnick, 1948

TRIO FOR FLUTE, VIOLA AND BASSOON   Opus 6
                                                              10'30"
I   Allegro ma non troppo – Presto
II   Andante con moto
III   Allegro commodo – Andante – Tempo primo
Score completed   London, date unknown
Autograph MS   untraced
First performance   Richard Adeney (fl), Wrayburn Glasspool (va), George
   Alexandra (bsn), Fyvie Hall, London, 18 January 1944 (Committee for
   the Promotion of New Music concert)
Publication   Paterson, 1954

1944

QUINTET FOR FLUTE, VIOLIN, VIOLA, HORN AND
BASSOON   Opus 7
I   Allegro con brio
II   Andante con moto
III   Allegretto con molto espressivo

Original Version duration unknown
Score completed London, date unknown
Autograph MS untraced
First performance Richard Adeney (fl), Albert Chasey (vn), Wrayburn
Glasspool (va), Charles Gregory (hn), George Alexandra (bsn),
National Gallery, London 21 December 1944 (National Gallery
Concert)

Revised Version 13'30"
Score completed details unknown
Autograph MS held by the Royal College of Music, London
First performance Geoffrey Gilbert (fl), Granville Jones (vn), Frederick
Riddle (va), Alan Civil (hn), Gwydion Brooke (bsn), Maida Vale
Studios, London, 8 March 1960 (BBC Invitation Concert)
Publication Paterson, 1960

20 TWO SONGS FOR VOICE AND PIANO Opus 8 5'00"
Text: Mei Sheng trs (I) Arthur Waley and (II) Maurice Carpenter
I *Neglected*: Allegro – Andante – Allegro
II *Morning Noon*: Andante con moto
Score completed London, date unknown
Autograph MS held by the Royal College of Music, London
First performance Joyce Newton (ms), Mabel Lovering (pno), Salle
Erard, London, 25 February 1947 (Committee for the Promotion of
New Music concert)

21 VARIATIONS ON A UKRAINIAN FOLK SONG
Opus 9 15'00"
for piano
Theme Andante con molto espressivo
I Molto agitato
II Allegro vivace
III Più mosso
IV Allegretto
V *Interlude*: Andante
VI Vivace
VII Allegretto semplice

VIII   Presto
IX   Andantino cantabile
X   *Fantasia*: con fuoco
Score completed   London, date unknown
Autograph MS   untraced
Dedication   John Kuchmy
First performance   Edith Vogel, Salle Erard, London, 19 November 1946
   (Committee for the Promotion of New Music concert)
Publication   Lengnick, 1948

Variations On a Ukrainian Folk Song was written at the suggestion of the
London Philharmonic Orchestra violinist, John Kuchmy, a Ukrainian.
The theme was later transformed into the popular song 'Yes, my darling
daughter'.

1945

2   DUO FOR FLUTE AND VIOLA   Opus 10   13'00"
I   Andante quasi allegretto
II   Allegro
III   Allegretto ma non troppo
Score completed   Ewhurst, Surrey, 18 March 1945
Autograph MS   held by the Royal College of Music, London
First performance   John Francis (fl), Bernard Davies (va), Salle Erard,
   London, 3 December 1946 (Committee for the Promotion of New
   Music concert)
Publication Faber Music, 1985

3   CONCERTO NO. 1 FOR HORN AND ORCHESTRA
Opus 11   22'00"
2+picc 2 2 2 – 0 0 0 0 – timp – str
I   Allegro commodo
II   Andante con moto
III   Allegro con brio
Score completed   London, 9 June 1945
Autograph MS   untraced

Dedication   Charles Gregory
First performance   Charles Gregory (hn)/London Philharmonic
   Orchestra/Ernest Ansermet, Royal Opera House, Covent Garden,
   London, 8 December 1946
Publication   Lengnick, 1947

24   SYMPHONIC SUITE FOR ORCHESTRA   Opus 12   15'00"
3 2 2 2 – 4 3 3 1 – timp 2perc – str
I   Allegro giubiloso
II   *Elegy:* Andante con moto
III   Andante moderato e molto sostenuto
Score completed   London, date unknown
Autograph MS   untraced (probably destroyed)
Dedication   written in memory of the composer's brother Philip, killed
   in the Second World War

Material from the first movement was subsequently incorporated into
the orchestral suite, *To Youth* (**33**), later published as *Little Suite* No. 1,
op. 53 (**73**).

25   PRELUDE FOR PIANO SOLO   2'00"
Andante con moto – Moderato e molto rubato – Andante con moto
Score completed   London, 18 December 1945
Autograph MSS   two copies, one inscribed 'With love from Malcolm,
   Xmas 1945', held by the Royal College of Music, London

1946

26   SYMPHONY FOR STRINGS   Opus 13   24'00"
I   Allegro ma non troppo
II   Andante quasi allegretto
III   Allegro feroce
Score completed   London, date unknown
Autograph MS   untraced
First performance   Riddick String Orchestra/Kathleen Riddick,
   Kensington Town Hall, London, 29 April 1947

First broadcast performance   Jacques Orchestra/Reginald Jacques, BBC
  Third Programme, 21 January 1948
Publication   Lengnick, 1947

Symphony for Strings was written for the Riddick String Orchestra.

FESTIVAL OVERTURE   Opus 14   6'00"
for orchestra
2 2 2 2 – 2 2 0 0 – timp – str
Score completed   London, date unknown
Autograph MS   untraced
First performance   Ipswich Symphony Orchestra/Philip Pfaff, Ipswich
  Town Hall, *c*1946

Festival Overture was written for Philip Pfaff.

1947

SONATA NO. 1 FOR VIOLIN AND PIANO   Opus 15 15'00"
I   Allegretto
II   Andante tranquillo – Allegro iracondamente – Tempo primo
III Allegro vivace – Presto
Score completed   London, 3 March 1947
Autograph MS   untraced
First performance   Nona Liddell (vn), Daphne Ibbott (pno), Arts Council
  Drawing Room, London, 2 October 1951 (Committee for the
  Promotion of New Music concert)
Publication   Lengnick, 1947

CHILDREN'S SUITE FOR PIANO   Opus 16   6'00"
I   *Prelude* (Study in Fourths and Fifths): Allegretto
II   *Carol* (Study in Legato Thirds for Left Hand): Andante con moto
III *Shepherd's Lament* (Study in Triplets and Accidentals): Andante con
     molto espressivo
IV   *Trumpet Tune* (Study in Trills and Rhythmic Playing): Allegro
V   *Blue Tune* (Study in Rhythms and Colour): Andante moderato
VI   *Folk Song* (Study in Touch and Phrasing): Allegro vivace

Score completed   details unknown
Autograph MS   untraced
Publication   Lengnick, 1948

30   SONATA FOR VIOLA AND PIANO   Opus 17   13'00"
I   Andante – Adagio – Tempo primo
II   Allegretto grazioso – Andante – Tempo primo
III Presto feroce – Adagio – Alla marcia – Andante – Presto feroce –
     Adagio – Prestissimo
Score completed   London, 30 March 1947
Autograph MS   untraced
Dedication   Frederick Riddle
First broadcast performance   Frederick Riddle (va), [pianist unknown],
     BBC Latin American Service, 1948
First British broadcast performance   Watson Forbes (va), Alan Richardson
     (pno); BBC Third Programme, 22 November 1949
Publication   Lengnick, 1948

31   TWO BAGATELLES FOR PIANO SOLO   Opus 18   4'00"
I   Allegretto
II   Moderato ma non allegro
Score completed   London, 29 September 1947
Autograph MS   held by the Royal College of Music, London
First performance   Richard Deering, British Music Information Centre,
     London, 15 May 1984

1948

32   SONATINA FOR FLUTE AND PIANO   Opus 19   8'00"
I   Allegro
II   Andante
III Allegretto languido
Score completed   London, 5 February 1948
Autograph MS   untraced
Dedication   Richard Adeney
First concert performance   details unknown

First broadcast performance   Richard Adeney (fl), Frederick Stone (pno),
   BBC Third Programme, 20 October 1952
Publication   Lengnick, 1948

TO YOUTH   9'30"
Suite for orchestra
2 2 2 2 – 4 3 3 1 – timp 2perc – str
I   *Prelude*: Maestoso
II   *Pastoral*: Allegretto
III   *March*: Allegro con brio
Score completed   London, date unknown
Autograph MS   held by the Royal College of Music, London
First performance   National Youth Orchestra of Great Britain/Reginald
   Jacques, The Pavilion, Bath, 21 April 1948
Publication   Paterson, 1956 (as *Little Suite for Orchestra* [*Little Suite* No. 1]
   op. 53, with the central movement retitled 'Dance')

The orchestral suite *To Youth* was written for the National Youth
Orchestra of Great Britain.

CONCERTO FOR CLARINET AND STRINGS
Opus 20   16'30"
I   Allegro
II   Andante con moto
III   Allegro con fuoco
Score completed   London, 15 February 1948
Autograph MS   full score untraced, reduction for clarinet and piano held
   by the Royal College of Music, London
Dedication   Frederick Thurston
First performance   Frederick Thurston (cl)/Jacques Orchestra/Reginald
   Jacques, Usher Hall, Edinburgh, 29 August 1949 (Edinburgh Festival)
First American performance   Benny Goodman (cl)/California Chamber
   Symphony Orchestra/Hendi Temianka, Royce Hall, University of
   California, Los Angeles, 2 October 1967
Publication   Lengnick, 1952

35   THE SMOKE   Opus 21   7'00"
Overture for orchestra
2+picc 2 2 2 – 4 3 3 1 – timp 3perc hp – str
Vivace ma non troppo – Andante con moto [alternating tempi]
Score completed   London, 19 July 1948
Autograph MS   held by the Royal College of Music, London
Dedication   Rudolf Schwarz and the Bournemouth Municipal Orchestra
First performance   Bournemouth Municipal Orchestra/Rudolf Schwarz,
   Royal Albert Hall, London, 24 October 1948
Publication   Lengnick, 1948

'The Smoke' is a cockney term for London.

1949

36   SYMPHONY NO. 1   Opus 22   28'30"
for orchestra
3 2 2 2 – 4 3 3 1 – timp perc hp – str
I   Allegro
II   Andantino
III   Vivace con fuoco – Alla marcia – Maestoso
Score completed   London, 16 February 1949
Autograph MS   held by the Royal College of Music, London
First performance   Hallé Orchestra/Malcolm Arnold, Cheltenham Town
   Hall, 6 July 1951 (Cheltenham Festival)
First London performance   London Philharmonic Orchestra/Malcolm
   Arnold, Royal Festival Hall, London, 16 November 1951
Publication   Lengnick, 1952

37   STRING QUARTET NO. 1   Opus 23   18'45"
I   Allegro commodo
II   Vivace
III   Andante – Lento – Tempo primo
IV   Allegro con spirito
Score completed   London, 19 August 1949
Autograph MS   untraced

First broadcast performance New London String Quartet, BBC Third
  Programme, 13 November 1950
First concert performance New London String Quartet, Institute of
  Contemporary Arts, London, 26 October 1951
Publication Lengnick, 1951

HENRI CHRISTOPHE
Opera [unfinished]
Libretto: Joe Mendoza
3 2 2 2 – 4 3 3 1 – timp 2perc hp – str
Characters Brelle (t), Vastey (bar), Phoebe (ms), Henri (b)
Setting the northern coast of Haiti, 1811
Autograph MS 205 bars (27 pages) in full score, including an Overture
  leading directly into Act I Scene 1, held by the Royal College of
  Music, London
Text complete libretto for Act I Scene 1, outline libretto for Act II
  Scene 2, copy of complete story and outline synopsis (26 pages), held
  by the RCM

Henri Christophe, the first black ruler of Haiti, shot himself with a
golden bullet when there was a popular uprising against him. The opera
was intended for the 1951 Festival of Britain but was turned down on
submission of the draft.

1950

DIVERTIMENTO NO. 2 Opus 24   9'00"
for orchestra
2+picc 2 2 2 – 4 3 3 1 – timp 2perc hp – str
I   *Fanfare*: Allegro
II   *Tango*: Lento
III *Chaconne*: Allegro con spirito
Score completed March 1950
Autograph MS untraced
First performance National Youth Orchestra of Great Britain/Reginald
  Jacques, The Dome, Brighton, 19 April 1950

First European performance   NYOGB/Reginald Jacques, Palais de
  Chaillot, Paris, April 1950
First broadcast performance   NYOGB/Walter Susskind, BBC Third
  Programme, 28 August 1950
First London performance   NYOGB/Hugo Rignold, Royal Albert Hall,
  London, 10 August 1957 (Henry Wood Promenade Concert)
Publication   see **105**

Divertimento No. 2 was written for the National Youth Orchestra of
Great Britain.

40   PSALM 150: LAUDATE DOMINUM   Opus 25   7′00″
   for s a t b chorus with organ
   Andantino – Allegretto – Allegro risoluto – Allargando – Lento –
     Andantino – Lento
   Score completed   6 April 1950
   Autograph MS   untraced
   Dedication   'To the Revd Canon Walter Hussey, the choir and organist
     of St Matthew's Church, Northampton'
   First performance   St Matthew's Church Choir/Philip Pfaff, St
     Matthew's Church, Northampton, 1950
   Publication   Lengnick, 1950

Arnold's setting of Psalm 150 was commissioned by St Matthew's
Church, Northampton.

41   SERENADE FOR SMALL ORCHESTRA   Opus 26   13′30″
   2 2 2 2 – 2 2 0 0 – timp – str
   I   Allegretto
   II   Andante con moto
   III   Allegro vivace
   Score completed   8 May 1950
   Autograph MS   held by the Royal College of Music, London
   First performance   New London Orchestra/Alec Sherman, The
     Orangery, Hampton Court, 4 June 1950
   Publication   Lengnick, 1950

ENGLISH DANCES (SET 1)   Opus 27   8'00"
for orchestra
2+picc 2 2 2 – 4 3 3 1 – timp 2perc cel hp – str
I   Andantino
II   Vivace
III   Mesto
IV   Allegro risoluto
Score completed   London, 5 December 1950
Autograph MS   untraced
Dedication   Bernard de Nevers (Lengnick)
First performance   London Philharmonic Orchestra/Sir Adrian Boult,
    Central Hall, East Ham, London, 14 April 1951
First broadcast performance   BBC Northern Orchestra/Charles Groves,
    BBC Home Service, 15 September 1951
Publication   Lengnick, 1951

This and a subsequent set of *English Dances* were later incorporated into
the ballet *Solitaire*. See **49** and **76**.

Piano Duet Arrangement (Franz Reizenstein)
Publication   Lengnick, 1958

Wind Band Arrangement (Maurice Johnstone)
Publication   Lengnick, 1965

1951

SONATINA FOR OBOE AND PIANO   Opus 28   7'30"
I   Leggiero
II   Andante con moto
III   Vivace
Score completed   London, 3 January 1951
Autograph MS   untraced
First performance   Leon Goossens (ob), John Wilson (pno), Northern
    College of Music, Manchester, 15 January 1952
Publication   Lengnick, 1951

44   UP AT THE VILLA [?1951]
Opera in one act [unfinished]
Libretto after Robert Browning

Joe Mendoza drafted a synopsis that formed the basis of Arnold's own
libretto for *Up at the Villa*. The libretto was originally intended for
William Walton, but Walton did not use it. Arnold made preliminary
sketches only for this work and subsequently destroyed them.

45   SONATINA FOR CLARINET AND PIANO   Opus 29   7'45″
I   Allegro con brio
II   Andantino
III   Furioso
Score completed   London, 18 January 1951
Autograph MS   untraced
First performance   Colin Davis (cl), Geoffrey Corbett (pno), Gallery of
   the Royal Society of British Artists, London, 20 March 1951
Publication   Lengnick, 1951

46   SYMPHONIC STUDY: 'MACHINES'   Opus 30   6'00″
for brass, percussion and strings
0 0 0 0 – 4 3 3 1 – timp 2perc – str
Theme: Allegro commodo
I   Vivace
II   Andante
III   Allegro con brio
IV   [Allegro con brio]
V   Allegro commodo – Lento e maestoso
Score completed   14 February 1951
Autograph MS   held by Faber Music
First performance   BBC Scottish Orchestra/Sir Charles Groves, Henry
   Wood Hall, Glasgow, 5 October 1984
First broadcast performance   as first performance, BBC Radio 3,
   16 October 1984
Publication   Faber Music, 1984

Machines is a reworking of the music for the documentary film *Report on
Steel* (**172**).

A SUSSEX OVERTURE Opus 31   8'30"
for orchestra
2+picc 2 2 2 – 4 3 3 1 – timp 2perc – str
Allegro con brio
Score completed London, 15 March 1951
Autograph MS untraced
Dedication Herbert Menges and the Brighton Philharmonic Society
First performance Southern Philharmonic Orchestra/Herbert Menges,
   The Dome, Brighton, 29 July 1951
Publication Lengnick, 1951

A Sussex Overture was commissioned for the 1951 Festival of Brighton.

CONCERTO FOR PIANO DUET AND STRINGS Opus 32
    21'30"

I   Allegro
II   Larghetto – Allegretto – Larghetto
III Vivace – Presto
Score completed London, 15 May 1951
Autograph MS held by the Royal College of Music, London
Dedication Helen Pyke and Paul Hamburger
First broadcast performance Helen Pyke, Paul Hamburger (pno)/
   Goldsbrough Orchestra/Mosco Carner, BBC Third Programme,
   17 August 1951
First London performance Helen Pyke, Paul Hamburger/London
   Symphony Orchestra/Basil Cameron, Royal Albert Hall, London,
   31 July 1953 (Henry Wood Promenade Concert)
Publication Lengnick, 1951

The Concerto for Piano Duet and Strings was composed at the
suggestion of Mosco Carner.

ENGLISH DANCES (SET 2) Opus 33   9'00"
for orchestra
2+picc 2 2 2 – 4 3 3 1 – timp 2perc cel hp – str
V   Allegro non troppo
VI   Con brio
VII Grazioso

VIII Giubiloso – Lento e maestoso
Score completed London, 26 June 1951
Autograph MS untraced
Dedication Bernard de Nevers (Lengnick)
First performance BBC Symphony Orchestra/Sir Malcolm Sargent,
   Royal Albert Hall, London, 5 August 1952 (Henry Wood Promenade
   Concert)
Publication Lengnick, 1951

This and an earlier set of *English Dances* were later incorporated into the
ballet *Solitaire*. See **42** and **76**.

49a Piano Duet Arrangement (Franz Reizenstein)
Publication Lengnick, 1958

1952

50 THE DANCING MASTER Opus 34   55′00″
Opera in one act
Libretto: Joe Mendoza after a play by William Wycherley
s ms a t t bbar
1+picc 2 2 2 – 4 3 3 1 – timp perc cel hp – str
Characters Miranda (s), Prue (ms), Mrs Caution (c), Monsieur (t),
   Gerard (t), Don Diego (bbar)
Setting Miranda's morning room on the first floor of a big house in
   London, 1664
Story Gerard, Miranda's lover, is discovered by her father, Don Diego,
   and passed off as a visiting dancing master with the connivance of her
   maid, Prue. Her aunt and her would-be spouse, a Frenchman, have
   their suspicions and try to convince Don Diego that he is being fooled.
   Soon the truth is out, but the Frenchman has meanwhile been beguiled
   by Prue and all ends happily.
Score completed London, 18 May 1952
Autograph MS held by the Royal College of Music, London
First performance (with piano reduction of orchestral parts only) Guelda
   Cunningham, Margaret Lindsay, Barbara Lane, David Barrett,

Donald Franke, Fergus O'Kelly, Lucy Reynolds (pno)/Herald Braune (choreography)/Jane Pearson-Gee and David Kentish (design), Barnes Music Club, Kitson Hall, Barnes, London, 1 March 1962

TWO CEREMONIAL PSALMS FOR TREBLE VOICES
Opus 35   5'00"
s s a
I   *O come, let us sing:* Maestoso
II   *Make a joyful noise:* Giubiloso
Score completed   details unknown
Autograph MS   untraced
First performance   Marble Arch Synagogue, London, 1952
Publication   Paterson, 1952

Two Ceremonial Psalms for Treble Voices was written for Anne Mendoza, sister of Joe Mendoza, librettist of *The Dancing Master* (**50**), and first performed at her wedding.

EIGHT CHILDREN'S PIECES FOR PIANO   Opus 36   8'00"
I   *Tired Bagpipes:* Slow
II   *Two Sad Hands:* Slow
III   *Across the Plains:* Slow
IV   *Strolling Tune:* Andantino
V   *Dancing Tune:* Allegro
VI   *Giants:* Pesante e poco lento
VII   *The Duke Goes A-Hunting:* Vivace
VIII   *The Buccaneer:* Vivace e con brio
Score completed   details unknown
Autograph MS   untraced
Publication   Lengnick, 1952

DIVERTIMENTO FOR WIND TRIO   Opus 37   8'45"
fl ob cl
I   Allegro energico
II   Languido
III   Vivace
IV   Andantino – Lento

V   Maestoso – Prestissimo
VI   Piacevole
Score completed   details unknown
Autograph MS   untraced
First performance   Richard Adeney (fl), Sidney Sutcliffe (ob), Stephen
     Waters (cl), Mercury Theatre, Notting Hill Gate, London, *c* 1953
Publication   Paterson, 1952

54   THE SOUND BARRIER   Opus 38   7'30"
Rhapsody for orchestra
3 2 2 2 – 4 3 3 1 – timp 2perc cel hp – str
Allegro moderato – Andantino – Vivace – Andante con moto – Lento –
     Molto vivace – Maestoso – Allargando
Score completed   London, 31 May 1952
Autograph MS   held by the Royal College of Music, London
First broadcast performance   Ulster Orchestra/Yannis Daras, BBC
     Radio 3, 23 May 1984
Publication   Paterson, 1952

The Sound Barrier is based on the main themes from the music for the
film of the same name (see **214**), and their development follows the story
line of the film.

55   CONCERTO FOR OBOE AND STRINGS   Opus 39   15'00"
I   Cantabile
II   Vivace
III   Quasi allegretto – Lento – Vivace
Score completed   London, 17 August 1952
Autograph MS   full score untraced, reduction for oboe and piano held by
     the Royal College of Music, London
Dedication   Leon Goossens
First performance   Leon Goossens (ob)/Boyd Neel Orchestra/Boyd Neel,
     Royal Festival Hall, London, 26 June 1953
First broadcast performance   Leon Goossens/Boyd Neel Orchestra/
     Anthony Collins, BBC Third Programme, 10 January 1954
Publication   Paterson, 1952

The Concerto for Oboe and Strings was commissioned by Leon Goossens.

1953

SYMPHONY NO. 2   Opus 40   30'00"
for orchestra
2+picc 2 2 2+cbsn – 4 3 3 1 – timp perc hp – str
I   Allegretto
II   Vivace
III   Lento
IV   Allegro con brio – Lento molto e maestoso
Score completed   London, 9 February 1953
Autograph MS   held by the British Library (MS 59797)
Dedication   Charles Groves and the Bournemouth Municipal Orchestra,
  in celebration of their Diamond Jubilee
First performance   Bournemouth Municipal Orchestra/Charles Groves,
  Winter Gardens, Bournemouth, 25 May 1953
First broadcast performance   BBC Scottish Orchestra/Alexander Gibson,
  BBC Third Programme, 9 February 1954
First European performance   L'Orchestre Symphonique de Grenoble/Eric-
  Paul Stekel, Grenoble, Switzerland, 4 March 1954
First Canadian performance   CBC Symphony Orchestra/John Avison,
  Vancouver, 26 April 1954
First London performance   London Philharmonic Orchestra/Malcolm
  Arnold, Royal Festival Hall, London, 3 June 1954
First American performance   Chicago Symphony Orchestra/Fritz Reiner,
  Civic Opera House, Chicago, 13 December 1956
First South African performance   Cape Town Orchestra/Anthony Collins,
  City Hall, Cape Town, 25 April 1957
First Australian performance   Sydney Symphony Orchestra/Sir Bernard
  Heinze, Town Hall, Sydney, 10 February 1963
Publication   Paterson, 1953

Symphony No. 2 was commissioned by the Winter Gardens Society,
Bournemouth. With it, Arnold's international reputation was
established.

SONATINA FOR RECORDER AND PIANO   Opus 41   7'45"
Alternative instrumentations   (i) flute and piano or (ii) oboe and piano

I   *Cantilena*: Piacevole
II   *Chaconne*: Andante con moto
III *Rondo*: Allegro vivace – Poco meno mosso – Tempo primo –
     Presto
Score completed   16 February 1953
Autograph MS   untraced
Dedication   Philip Rodgers
First broadcast performance   Philip Rodgers (rec), Albert Hardie (pno),
    BBC Home Service, Manchester, 14 July 1953
First concert performance   details unknown
Publication   Paterson, 1953

The Sonatina for Recorder and Piano was written for Philip Rodgers.

58   KATHERINE, WALKING AND RUNNING   0'40"
for two violins
Allegretto
Score completed   details unknown
Autograph MS   held by Katherine King

Arnold wrote *Katherine, Walking and Running* for his daughter Katherine
to play with a school friend.

59   HOMAGE TO THE QUEEN   Opus 42   40'00"
Ballet for orchestra
2+picc 2 2 2 – 4 3 3 1 – timp 2perc cel hp – str
I   *Prelude and opening scene*
II   *Earth*: Girl's variation – Man's variation – Finale
III *Water*: Moderato – Man's variation – Girl's variation – Pas de deux
IV   *Fire*: Pas de deux – Girl's variation – Man's variation – Finale
V   *Air*: Man's variation – Pas de deux – Finale
Score completed   London, May 1953
Autograph MS   untraced
First performance   Orchestra of the Royal Opera House, Covent
    Garden/Robert Irving/Sadler's Wells Theatre Ballet: Nadia Nerina
    (Queen of the Earth), Alexis Rassine (her Consort), Pauline Clayden,
    Margaret Dale, Anne Heaton, Michael Boulton, Peter Clegg, Ray
    Powell (Pas de Six), Violetta Elvin (Queen of the Water), John Hart

(her Consort), Brian Shaw, Julia Farron, Rowena Jackson (Pas de Trois), Beryl Grey (Queen of Fire), John Field (her Consort), Alexander Grant (Spirit of Fire), Svetlana Beriosova, Rosemary Lindsay, Brian Ashbridge, Philip Chatfield (Pas de Quatre), Margot Fonteyn (Queen of the Air), Michael Somes (her Consort)/Frederick Ashton (choreography), Oliver Messel (design), John Sullivan (lighting); Royal Opera House, Covent Garden, London, 2 June 1953
First American performance   Metropolitan Opera House, New York, September 1953
Publication   Paterson, 1953

Homage to the Queen is, in a sense, four ballets in one. Each of the main sections is a vehicle for a choreographic display by one of the Four Elements, each represented by a Queen, her Consort and an attendant Court. The ballet concludes with an apotheosis of 'homage' to Elizabeth I and the newly crowned Elizabeth II.

0   HOMAGE TO THE QUEEN BALLET SUITE   Opus 42a
for orchestra   17'00"
2+picc 2 2 2 – 4 3 3 1 – timp 2perc cel hp – str
Air: Man's variation – Pas de deux – Finale
Score completed   details unknown
Autograph MS   untraced
First performance   London Philharmonic Orchestra/Malcolm Arnold, New Theatre, Northampton, 19 July 1953
First broadcast performance   BBC Northern Symphony Orchestra/ Stanford Robinson, BBC Light Programme, 13 May 1957

a   Military Band Arrangement (Finale only) (F. Vivian Dunn)

1   HOMAGE TO THE QUEEN   Opus 42b   9'00"
Suite for piano solo
I   *Earth: Girl's variation*: Allegretto
II   *Water*: Waltz and Allegretto
III   *The Spirit of Fire*: Allegro con brio
IV   *The Queen of the Air*: Allegretto grazioso
V   *Pas de deux*: Adagio non troppo

VI   *Homage march*: Marziale – Allargando
Score completed   details unknown
Autograph MS   untraced
Publication   Paterson, 1954

62   SONATA NO. 2 FOR VIOLIN AND PIANO   Opus 43   9′00″
Allegretto – Vivace – Andantino quasi allegretto – Adagio molto
Score completed   details unknown
Autograph MS   untraced
First performance   Suzanne Rozsa (vn), Paul Hamburger (pno), Recital
   Room, Royal Festival Hall, London, 21 October 1953
Publication   Paterson, 1953

63   FLOURISH FOR A 21ST BIRTHDAY   Opus 44   3′00″
for brass and percussion
0 0 0 0 – 4 3+2cnt 3 1 – timp 3perc
Allegro giubiloso – Meno mosso – Tempo primo
Score completed   details unknown
Autograph MS   held by the London Philharmonic Orchestra Library
Dedication   'To Sir Adrian Boult and the LPO in celebration of the 21st
   anniversary of the foundation of the orchestra'
First performance   London Philharmonic Orchestra/Sir Adrian Boult,
   Royal Albert Hall, London, 7 October 1953
Publication   Studio Music, 1986

1954

64   CONCERTO FOR FLUTE AND STRINGS   Opus 45   12′30″
I   Allegro energico
II   Andante
III   Con fuoco – Presto
Score completed   London, 3 February 1954
Autograph MS   full score and reduction for flute and piano, held by the
   Royal College of Music, London
Dedication   Richard Adeney
First performance   Richard Adeney (fl)/Boyd Neel Orchestra/John

Hollingsworth, Victoria and Albert Museum, London, 11 April 1954
First broadcast performance   Richard Adeney (fl)/London Chamber
   Orchestra/Anthony Bernard, BBC Third Programme, 3 September
   1954
Publication   Paterson, 1954

The Concerto for Flute and Strings was written for Richard Adeney.

5   CONCERTO FOR HARMONICA AND
   ORCHESTRA   Opus 46   9′00″
   0 0 0 0 – 4 3 3 1 – timp 2perc – str
   I   Grazioso
   II   Mesto
   III   Con brio – Presto
Score completed   26 June 1954
Autograph MS   held by the Royal College of Music, London
Dedication   Larry Adler
First performance   Larry Adler (harm)/BBC Symphony Orchestra/
   Malcolm Arnold, Royal Albert Hall, London, 14 August 1954
   (Henry Wood Promenade Concert)
Publication   Paterson, 1954

The Concerto for Harmonica and Orchestra was commissioned by the
BBC and written for Larry Adler.

6   CONCERTO FOR ORGAN AND ORCHESTRA   Opus 47
                                                                  12′30″
   0 0 0 0 – 0 1+2(in D) 0 0 – timp – str
   I   Vivace
   II   Lento
   III   Allegretto
Score completed   October 1954
Autograph MS   held by the Royal College of Music, London
First performance   Denis Vaughan (org)/London Symphony
   Orchestra/Leslie Woodgate, Royal Festival Hall, London,
   11 December 1954 (Robert Mayer concert)
Publication   Paterson, 1954

The Concerto for Organ and Orchestra was written for Denis Vaughan and specially composed for the organ of the Royal Festival Hall, London.

67 SINFONIETTA NO. 1   Opus 48   12'00"
for orchestra
0 2 0 0 – 2 0 0 0 – str
I   Allegro commodo
II   Allegretto
III   Allegro con brio
Score completed   October 1954
Autograph MS   held by the Royal College of Music, London
Dedication   Boyd Neel Orchestra
First performance   Boyd Neel Orchestra/Anthony Collins, Albert Hall, Nottingham, 3 December 1954
First London performance   Boyd Neel Orchestra/Anthony Collins, Royal Festival Hall, London, 7 March 1955
First British broadcast performance   Francis Chagrin Ensemble/Francis Chagrin, BBC Home Service, 11 April 1957 (The work was broadcast on French radio three times before the first British transmission.)
Publication   Paterson, 1955

68 RINALDO AND ARMIDA   Opus 49   23'00"
Ballet for orchestra
2+picc 2 2 2 – 4 3 3 1 – timp 2perc cel hp – str
Story   The enchantress Armida lures lovers into her sinister garden. Those whose love she does not return must die, but if she returns their love she herself must accept death as the consequence. Rinaldo, drawn into her domain, falls victim to her spell. Sibilla warns Armida that returning Rinaldo's love will bring about her death. Unheeding, Armida surrenders herself to Rinaldo and dies in his arms. A storm breaks and Rinaldo flees in terror.
Score completed   31 December 1954
Autograph MS   full score untraced, piano reduction held by the Royal Opera House, Covent Garden
First performance   Orchestra of the Royal Opera House, Covent Garden/Malcolm Arnold/Sadler's Wells Theatre Ballet: Michael Somes (Rinaldo), Svetlana Beriosova (Armida), Julia Farron (Sibilla),

Ronald Hynd (Gandolfo)/Frederick Ashton (choreography), Peter
Rue (design), John Sullivan (lighting); Royal Opera House, Covent
Garden, London, 6 January 1955

1955

SERENADE FOR GUITAR AND STRINGS   Opus 50   5′30″
Andante – Allegretto – Allegro – Allegretto – Andante
Score completed   February 1955
Autograph MS   full score untraced, reduction for guitar and piano held
   by the Royal College of Music, london
Dedication   Julian Bream
First performance   Julian Bream (gtr)/Richmond Community Centre
   String Orchestra/Malcolm Arnold, Richmond Community Centre
   ' Hall, Richmond, Surrey, Summer 1955
First London performance   Julian Bream/Kalmar Chamber Orchestra/
   Leonard Friedman, Wigmore Hall, London, 11 June 1956
Publication   Paterson, 1955

The Serenade for Guitar and Strings was written for Julian Bream.

TAM O'SHANTER   Opus 51   7′30″
Overture for orchestra
2+picc 2 2 2 – 4 3 3 1 – timp 2perc – str
Poco lento – Allegretto – Vivace – Allegretto – Allegro – Allegretto –
   Andante con moto – Allegro e sempre accelerando al presto – Vivace –
   Lento molto – Presto
Score completed   2 March 1955
Autograph MS   held by the National Library of Scotland
Dedication   Michael Diack (Paterson)
First performance   Royal Philharmonic Orchestra/Malcolm Arnold,
   Royal Albert Hall, London, 16 August 1955 (Henry Wood Promenade
   Concert)
First Scottish performance   Scottish National Orchestra/Alexander
   Gibson, Usher Hall, Edinburgh, 23 March 1956
Publication   Paterson, 1955

71   FANFARE FOR A FESTIVAL   2'00"
for brass and percussion
0 0 0 0 – 4 3+cnt 3 1 – timp 3perc
Allegro
Score completed   April 1955
Autograph MS   held by the London Philharmonic Orchestra Library
Publication   Studio Music, 1986

Fanfare for a Festival was written for the Hastings Festival.

72   JOHN CLARE CANTATA   Opus 52   11'00"
for s a t b chorus and piano duet
Texts: John Clare
I   *Winter Snow Storm*: Andantino
II   *March*: Allegro non troppo
III   *Spring*: Allegretto
IV   *Summer*: Allegro
V   *Autumn*: Andante
VI   *Epilogue*: Andantino
Score completed   details unknown
Autograph MS   held by Isobel Arnold
First performance   Summer School Choir/Viola Tunnard and Martin
        Penny (pnos)/John Clements, Dartington Hall, Devon, 5 August 1955
First broadcast performance   BBC Chorus/Viola Tunnard and Martin
        Penny/Alexander Gibson, BBC Third Programme (in collaboration
        with the Institute of Contemporary Arts, London), 16 April 1956
Publication   Paterson, 1956

John Clare, like Arnold, was born in Northampton. *John Clare Cantata* is
thus a tribute from one Northamptonshire artist to another. It was
commissioned by William Glock for the 1955 Dartington Summer
School of Music.

73   LITTLE SUITE NO. 1   Opus 53   9'30"
for orchestra
2 2 2 2 – 4 3 3 1 – timp 2perc – str
I   *Prelude*: Maestoso
II   *Dance*: Allegretto

III   *March*: Allegro con brio
Publication   Paterson, 1956

See *To Youth* (**33**).

3a   Military Band Arrangement [March only] (Peter Sumner)   2'30"
Publication   Paterson, 1965

1956

74   PIANO TRIO   Opus 54   12'30"
vn vc pno
I   Allegro con fuoco
II   Andante
III   Vivace energico
Score completed   details unknown
Autograph MS   untraced
Dedication   Pauline Howgill
First performance   St Cecilia Trio: Pauline Howgill, Sylvia Cleaver,
     Norman Jones; International Music Association, London, 30 April
     1956
First broadcast performance   St Cecilia Trio, BBC Home Service,
     7 September 1956
Publication   Paterson, 1956

5   SONG OF PRAISE   Opus 55   4'00"
for unison voices (with optional descant) and piano
Alternative instrumentations   unison voices (with optional descant) and
     (i) strings and piano *or* (ii) orchestra
Text: John Clare
Orchestral version
1 1 1 1 – 2 2 2 0 – timp perc org – str
Allegro moderato e maestoso
Score completed   details unknown
Autograph MS   orchestral version held by the Royal College of Music,
     London

First performance   details unknown
Publication   Paterson, 1956

Song of Praise was commissioned by Ruth Railton, who also conducted
the first performance. The work was written for the jubilee of Wycombe
Abbey School.

76   SOLITAIRE   25′30″
Ballet for orchestra
Note   The music for *Solitaire* comprises the two sets of *English Dances*
   (**42** and **49**) and two newly composed dances, *Sarabande* and *Polka*.
2+picc 2 2 2 – 4 3 3 1 – timp 2perc cel hp – str
I   Grazioso (*E.D.* VII)
II   Andantino (*E.D.* I)
III   Vivace (*E.D.* II)
IV   Mesto (*E.D.* III)
V   Allegro risoluto (*E.D.* IV)
VI   *Sarabande*: Andantino
VII   *Polka*: Allegro non troppo
VIII   Con brio (*E.D.* VI)
IX   Allegro non troppo (*E.D.* V)
X   Giubiloso – Lento e maestoso (*E.D.* VIII)
XI   Grazioso (*E.D.* VII)
Score completed   details unknown
Autograph MS   untraced
First performance   Sadler's Wells Theatre Orchestra/John
   Lanchberry/Sadler's Wells Theatre Ballet: Margaret Hill, Sara Neil,
   Donald Macleary, Brenda Bolton, Donald Britton, Michael
   Boulton/Kenneth MacMillan (choreography), Desmond Heeley
   (design); Sadler's Wells Theatre, London, 7 June 1956
Publication   Paterson, 1956

Solitaire was described by its choreographer, Kenneth MacMillan,
as 'a kind of game for one'. The central character is a girl who tries
desperately to become involved in the playground games of her friends
but always ends up on her own.

Piano Solo Arrangement (Sarabande and Polka only) (arranger
unknown) 7'30"
Publication Paterson, 1959

Symphonic Band Arrangement (Sarabande and Polka only) (John
Paynter)
Publication Paterson and Carl Fischer, 1983

7 FANFARE FOR A ROYAL OCCASION 1'20"
for brass
3tpt 3trb
Allegro brillante
Score completed details unknown
Autograph MS held by the BBC Music Library (ref. 22889)
First performance Trumpeters of the Royal Military School of Music,
Kneller Hall/Lt.-Col. David McBain, Royal Festival Hall, London,
19 November 1956 (St Cecilia's Day concert)
Publication Studio Music, 1986

8 THE OPEN WINDOW Opus 56 21'30"
Opera in one act
Libretto: Sidney Gilliat after a short story by Saki
s s ms t bar bar
fl cl bsn hn hp perc 2vn va vc db
Characters The maid (s), Mr Nuttel (t), Vera – a young girl (s), Alice
Sappleton – Vera's aunt (ms), Edward Sappleton – Vera's uncle (bar),
Jack – Mrs Sappleton's brother (bar)
Setting a pleasant drawing room of a small manor house in the country;
the time is the present, on a sunny afternoon in October
Story a comedy about a repressed bank clerk, Mr Nuttel, who enjoys
bad health and goes to the country to convalesce from the threat of a
nervous breakdown
Score completed details unknown
Autograph MS full score and vocal score, held by the Royal College of
Music, London
First broadcast performance Ethel Lyon, John Carolan, June Bronhill,
Flora Nielsen, Niven Miller, David Oddie/English Opera Group

Orchestra/Lionel Salter/George Fox (direction), Richard Wilmot (design), BBC Television, 14 December 1956
First staged performance Lincoln Opera Group/Lionel Barnby, Horton-cum-Beckering Country Theatre, April 1958

79 A GRAND, GRAND OVERTURE Opus 57 8'00"
for orchestra
3 vacuum cleaners 1 floor polisher 4 rifles –
2+picc 2 2 2 – 4 3 3 1 – timp 2perc org hp – str
Allegro con brio – Molto meno mosso e maestoso – Presto
Score completed 19 October 1956
Autograph MS untraced
First performance Morley College Symphony Orchestra with Dennis Brain (org)/Malcolm Arnold, Royal Festival Hall, London, 13 November 1956
Publication Paterson, 1956

A Grand, Grand Overture was written for the 1956 Hoffnung Music Festival.

79a Symphonic Band Arrangement (Keith Wilson)
Publication Paterson and Carl Fischer, 1983

80 CONCERTO NO. 2 FOR HORN AND STRINGS Opus 58
13'30"

I   Con energico
II   Andante grazioso
III Vivace – Presto
Score completed 15 December 1956
Autograph MS held by Annetta Hoffnung
Dedication Dennis Brain
First performance Dennis Brain (hn)/Hallé Orchestra/Malcolm Arnold, Cheltenham Town Hall, 17 July 1957 (Cheltenham Festival)
Publication Paterson, 1956

1957

FOUR SCOTTISH DANCES   Opus 59   8'30"
for orchestra
1+picc 2 2 2 – 4 2 3 0 – timp perc hp – str
I   Pesante
II   Vivace
III   Allegretto
IV   Con brio
Score completed   February 1957
Autograph MS   untraced
First performance   BBC Concert Orchestra/Malcolm Arnold, Royal
   Festival Hall, London, 8 June 1957
Publication   Paterson, 1957

Four Scottish Dances was commissioned for the BBC Light Music
Festival.

Brass Band Arrangement (Ray Farr)
First performance   Manger Brass Band/Michael Antrobus, Usher Hall,
   Edinburgh, 6 May 1984
Publication   Paterson 1984

HRH THE DUKE OF CAMBRIDGE   Opus 60   3'30"
March for military band
Dbpicc fl ob Ebcl 2cl bsn asax tsax 2cnt 2hn 3trb euph bass cym sd
   6heraldtpt
Allegro con spirito
Score completed   details unknown
Autograph MS   held by the Royal Military School of Music, Kneller
   Hall
Dedication   Lt.-Col. David McBain
First performance   Band of the Royal Military School of Music, Kneller
   Hall/Rodney Bashford (Bandmaster), Kneller Hall, Twickenham,
   28 June 1957
Publication   Paterson and Carl Fischer, 1957

The Royal Military School of Music at Kneller Hall was founded in 1857 by the Duke of Cambridge, then Commander-in-Chief of the British Army. This march was written to celebrate the School's centenary in 1957.

83 OBOE QUARTET Opus 61   12′45″
ob vn va vc
I   Allegro non troppo
II   Allegretto
III   Vivace con brio
Score completed   2 April 1957
Autograph MS   score untraced, sketch only (with alternative opening 14 bars deleted) held by the Royal College of Music, London
Dedication   Leon Goossens
First performance   Leon Goosens (ob), Carter String Trio: Mary Carter (vn), Anatole Mines (va), Eileen McCarthy (vc), Cambridge University Music School, 2 May 1957
First broadcast performance   Leon Goossens, Carter String Trio, BBC Third Programme, 18 June 1958
Publication   Faber Music, 1966

Originally titled 'Serenade for Oboe Quartet', the Oboe Quartet was written for Leon Goossens on the occasion of his sixtieth birthday.

84 TOY SYMPHONY Opus 62   9′30″
12 toy instruments: quail cuckoo whistle 3tpt 3dulc trgl cym drum – pno – strqt (or str)
I   Allegro
II   Allegretto
III   Vivace
Score completed   London, 25 July 1957
Autograph MS   held by the Royal College of Music, London
Dedication   The Musicians' Benevolent Fund
First performance   Alderman Sir Denis Truscott, Dr Thomas Armstrong, Edric Cundell, Dr W. Greenhouse Alt, Gerard Hoffnung, Eileen Joyce, Sir Steuart Wilson, George Baker, Col. David McBain, Leslie Woodgate, Eric Coates, Astra Desmond, Amici String Quartet, Joseph Cooper (pno)/Malcolm Arnold, Savoy Hotel, London,

28 November 1957 (St Cecilia Festival Dinner)
First broadcast performance   BBC Scottish Orchestra/Colin Davis, [details
of network unknown], 1 April 1958
Publication   Paterson, 1958

5   SYMPHONY NO. 3   Opus 63   32'30"
for orchestra
2+picc 2 2 2 – 4 3 3 1 – timp – str
I   Allegro – Vivace
II   Lento
III   Allegro con brio – Presto – Lento e maestoso – Presto
Score completed   details unknown
Autograph MS   held by the Royal College of Music, London
Dedication   the Royal Liverpool Philharmonic Society
First performance   Royal Liverpool Philharmonic Orchestra/John
Pritchard, Royal Festival Hall, London, 2 December 1957
First Liverpool performance   RLPO/John Pritchard, Philharmonic Hall,
10 December 1957
First broadcast performance   RLPO/John Pritchard, BBC Home Service,
25 April 1958
Publication   Paterson, 1958

Symphony No. 3 was commissioned by the Royal Liverpool
Philharmonic Society.

COMMONWEALTH CHRISTMAS OVERTURE   Opus 64
14'30"
for orchestra
2+picc 2 2 2 – 4 3 3 1 – timp 4perc cel hp – str (+ 3gtr mrmb Afro-Cuban
perc group)
Allegro giubiloso – Allegretto – Moderato – Allegro giubiloso
Score completed   London, 17 November 1957
Autograph MS   held by the BBC Music Library (ref. 22449)
First broadcast performance   BBC Symphony Orchestra/Rudolf Schwarz,
BBC Television, 25 December 1957

Commonwealth Christmas Overture was commissioned by the BBC for the

1957 *Christmas Round the World* programme, marking the twenty-fifth anniversary of the first Christmas broadcast by a British monarch.

87 RICHMOND 0'36"
Fanfare for brass
3tpt 3trb
Moderato e maestoso
Score completed   details unknown
Autograph MS   untraced
First public performance   Fanfare trumpeters of the Royal Military School of Music, Kneller Hall/Rodney Bashford (bandmaster), Richmond, Surrey, Christmas 1957
Publication   Studio Music, 1986

Richmond was commissioned by the BBC as part of the Royal Prologue music for the 1957 *Christmas Round the World* programme (see also **86** & **292**).

1958

88 SINFONIETTA NO. 2   Opus 65 12'30"
for orchestra
2000–2000–str
I   Allegro non troppo
II   Lento
III   Allegro con brio
Score completed   26 May 1958
Autograph MS   held by the Royal College of Music, London
Dedication   'For J' [Reginald Jacques]
First performance   Jacques Orchestra/Reginald Jacques, Victoria and Albert Museum, London, 15 June 1958
First broadcast performance   Jacques Orchestra/Reginald Jacques, BBC Home Service, 15 July 1959
Publication   Paterson, 1958

Sinfonietta No. 2 was written for the twenty-first anniversary of the Jacques Orchestra.

CONCERT PIECE FOR PERCUSSION 4'30"
for 3 percussion players and piano
pno 3timp sd bd cym tamb t-t wdbl trgl xyl glsp whip mrcs bong
Allegro moderato ma maestoso – Allegro con brio – Vivace – Più mosso
 – Molto vivace
Score completed 1 June 1958
Autograph MS held by James Blades
Dedication James Blades
First performance details unknown
Publication Faber Music, 1984

Concert Piece for Percussion was written for BBC Television.

Arrangement for 1 Percussion Player and Piano (James Blades)
Publication Faber Music, 1984

UNITED NATIONS 13'00"
for 4 military bands, organ and orchestra
2+picc 2 2 2 – 4 3 3 1 – timp 3perc – str
Andante con moto – Allegro con energico – Andante con moto
Score completed details unknown
Autograph MS held by the Royal College of Music, London
First performance Band of the Royal Military School of Music, Kneller
 Hall/Morley College Symphony Orchestra/Malcolm Arnold, Royal
 Festival Hall, London, 21 November 1958

United Nations was commissioned for the 1958 Hoffnung Interplanetary
Music Festival.

1959 ·

FIVE WILLIAM BLAKE SONGS Opus 66 12'30"
for alto and strings
I *O Holy Virgin! Clad in purest white*: Moderato
II *Memory, hither come and tune your merry notes*: Allegro
III *How sweet I roam'd from field to field*: Allegretto
IV *My silks and fine array*: Andante con moto

V   *Thou fair-hair'd angel of the evening*: Lento
Score completed   details unknown
Autograph MS   untraced
Dedication   Pamela Bowden
First performance   Pamela Bowden(a)/Richmond Community Centre
    String Orchestra/Malcolm Arnold, Richmond Community Centre
    Hall, Surrey, 26 March 1959
First London performance   Pamela Bowden/Jacques Orchestra/Reginald
    Jacques, Victoria and Albert Museum, London, 12 July 1959
Publication   British & Continental Music Agencies, 1966

Five William Blake Songs was written for Pamela Bowden.

92   FOUR PIECES FOR CHAMBER ENSEMBLE   4'00"
rec 3vn
I   *Prelude*: Allegro moderato
II   *Waltz*: Allegro
III   *Chorale*: Andante
IV   *Carillon*: Allegro moderato
Score completed   details unknown
Autograph MS   score and parts, held by Katherine King

Four Pieces for Chamber Ensemble was written as practice material for
the Arnold family.

**93   CONCERTO FOR GUITAR AND CHAMBER
ORCHESTRA   Opus 67**   21'30"
fl cl hn vn va vc db
I   Allegro
II   Lento
III   Con brio
Score completed   details unknown
Autograph MS   untraced
Dedication   Julian Bream
First broadcast performance   Julian Bream (gtr)/Melos Ensemble/Malcolm
    Arnold, BBC Third Programme, 18 June 1959
First concert performance   Julian Bream/Melos Ensemble/Malcolm
    Arnold, Jubilee Hall, Aldeburgh, 25 June 1959 (Aldeburgh Festival)

Improvising jazz on a Thomas Goff clavichord with guitarist Julian Bream (1958).

First London performance   Julian Bream/Melos Ensemble/Malcolm
  Arnold, Victoria and Albert Museum, 6 March 1960
Publication   Paterson, 1961

The Concerto for Guitar and Chamber Orchestra was commissioned by
Julian Bream. The slow movement is dedicated to the memory of the
jazz guitarist Django Reinhardt.

94   KINGSTON FANFARE   0'25"
  for brass
  3tpt 3trb
  Score completed   details unknown
  Autograph MS   held by the Royal Military School of Music, Kneller
    Hall
  Publication   Studio Music, 1986

95   SWEENEY TODD   Opus 68   23'00"
  Ballet for orchestra
  1+picc 1 2 1 – 2 2 2 0 – timp perc pno cel hp – str
  Score completed   London, 5 November 1959
  Autograph MS   full score held by the Royal Opera House, Covent
    Garden, piano reduction held by the Royal College of Music, London
  First performance   Orchestra of the Royal Opera House, Covent
    Garden/John Lanchberry/Royal Ballet: Donald Britton (Sweeney
    Todd), Gordon Aitken (Sergeant Lightfoot), Margaret Knoesen (Mrs
    Lovett), Simon Mottram (Man with watch), Johaar Mosaval (Tobias),
    Elizabeth Anderton (Johanna), Shirley Bishop (Johanna's mother),
    Jeffrey Phillips (a sailor), Desmond Doyle (Mark Ingestre), Ian
    Hamilton (Colonel Jeffrey), Terry Westmoreland, Robert Mead,
    Michael Coleman, Colin Jones, Alan Beale, Alan Alder, Adrian
    Grater, Kathleen Geldard (policemen)/John Cranko (choreography),
    Alix Stone (design), William Bundy (lighting); Shakespeare Memorial
    Theatre, Stratford-upon-Avon, 10 December 1959
  First London performance   Royal Ballet, Royal Opera House, Covent
    Garden, 16 August 1960

SWEENEY TODD: CONCERT SUITE FOR
ORCHESTRA   Opus 68a   12'00"
1+picc 1 2 1 – 2 2 2 0 – timp perc pno cel hp – str

The *Sweeney Todd* Concert Suite was drawn from the complete ballet
score (**95**) in 1984 by David Ellis in association with the composer.

SONG OF SIMEON   Opus 69   29'30"
Nativity masque for mimes, soloists, mixed chorus and orchestra
Text: Christopher Hassall
0 0 0 0 – 0 3 3 1 – timp 2perc cel hp – str
Alternative instrumentation   rec pno duet timp perc str
Prelude: Andante con moto
Scene: the place of the annunciation
Scene: the inn at Bethlehem
Scene: outside the temple of Jerusalem
Score completed   London, 5 December 1959
Autograph MS   full score and vocal score, held by the Royal College of
   Music, London
First performance   Nicholas Chagrin, Imogen Hassall (mimes)/St
   Martin's Singers and Concert Orchestra/Malcolm Arnold/Colin
   Graham (direction), John Cranko (choreography), Annena Stubbs
   (design), Drury Lane Theatre, London, 5 January 1960
Publication   Oxford University Press, 1960, Faber Music, 1986

Song of Simeon was written for a charity matinée for the Church of
St Martin-in-the-Fields, which each Christmas raised funds in aid of
refugee work. In 1960 the money raised (£3,000) went to benefit the
training school for refugee children at Spittal in Austria.

THE PILGRIM CARAVAN   2'30"
Excerpt from *Song of Simeon* (**97**)

Arrangement for unaccompanied voices
s a t b
Autograph MS   untraced
Publication   Oxford University Press, 1960

Arrangement for unison voices (with optional descant) and piano and
strings *or* orchestra
2 2 2 2 – 2 3 3 0 – 2perc pno timp (optional pno and str)
Autograph MS   orchestral score, held by the Royal College of Music,
London
Publication   Oxford University Press, 1960, Faber Music, 1986

1960

99   MARCH: 'OVERSEAS'   Opus 70   2'30"
for military band
Dbpicc Cpicc fl ob Ebcl 3cl acl bcl bsn 2asax tsax barsax 3cnt 4Ebhn
4hn 3trb 2bar 2tuba blra timp cym bd (with doubling on fl, cl, cnt, hn,
tuba and drums where necessary)
Score completed   details unknown
Autograph MS   untraced
First performance   [personnel unknown], New York, 1960
Publication   Paterson and Carl Fischer, 1960

Overseas was commissioned by the Central Office of Information for the
British Trade Fair, New York, in 1960.

100   SYMPHONY NO. 4   Opus 71   36'00"
for orchestra
2+picc 2 2 2+cbsn – 4 3 3 1 – timp 3perc cel hp – str
I   Allegro
II   Vivace ma non troppo
III   Andantino
IV   Con fuoco – Alla marcia – Tempo primo – Maestoso – Allegro
       molto
Score completed   13 July 1960
Autograph MS   held by the Royal College of Music, London
First performance   BBC Symphony Orchestra/Malcolm Arnold, Royal
Festival Hall, London, 2 November 1960
Publication   Paterson, 1960

Symphony No. 4 was commissioned by the BBC.

CARNIVAL OF ANIMALS   Opus 72   15'00"
for orchestra
2+picc 2 2 2 – 4 3 3 1 – timp 2perc – str
I   *The Giraffe*: Allegretto
II   *Sheep*: Poco lento
III   *Cows*: Moderato
IV   *Mice*: Vivace
V   *Jumbo*: Andante
VI   *Chiroptera*
Score completed   details unknown
Autograph MS   held by the Royal College of Music, London
First performance   Morley College Symphony Orchestra/Malcolm
    Arnold, Royal Festival Hall, London, 31 October 1960

Carnival of Animals was commissioned for the Hoffnung Memorial
Concert.

A HOFFNUNG FANFARE   2'00"
for brass and percussion
36 herald trumpets (in 6 groups of 6) – sd bd timp
Brillante ma non troppo allegro
Score completed   details unknown
Autograph MS   held by Annetta Hoffnung
First performance   Trumpeters of the Royal Military School of Music,
    Kneller Hall, Royal Festival Hall, London, 31 October 1960

A Hoffnung Fanfare was written for the Hoffnung Memorial Concert.

1961

QUINTET FOR BRASS   Opus 73   13'00"
2tpt hn trb tuba
I   Allegro vivace
II   *Chaconne*: Andante con moto
III   Con brio
Score completed   23 January 1961
Autograph MS   held by the Royal College of Music, London

Dedication   New York Brass Quintet
First performance   New York Brass Quintet, New York, 1961
First British performance   Francis Chagrin Ensemble, London, 17 March
   1962 (St Pancras Festival)
Publication   Paterson, 1961

The Quintet for Brass was written for the New York Brass Quintet.

104   S Y M P H O N Y N O. 5   Opus 74   33′00″
for orchestra
2+picc 2 2 2 – 4 3 3 1 – timp 2perc cel hp – str
I   Tempestuoso
II   Andante con moto – Adagio
III   Con fuoco
IV   Risoluto – Lento
Score completed   Richmond, London, 7 May 1961
Autograph MS   held by Cheltenham Public Library
First performance   Hallé Orchestra/Malcolm Arnold, Cheltenham
   Town Hall, Cheltenham, 3 July 1961 (Cheltenham Festival)
First broadcast performance   BBC Northern Symphony Orchestra/Malcolm
   Arnold, BBC Music Programme, 1 May 1967
First London performance   New Philharmonia Orchestra/Malcolm
   Arnold, Royal Festival Hall, London, 16 December 1971
Publication   Paterson, 1960

Symphony No. 5 was commissioned by the Cheltenham Festival
Society.

105   D I V E R T I M E N T O N O. 2   Opus 75   9′00″
for orchestra
2+picc 2 2 2 – 4 3 3 1 – timp 2perc hp – str
I   *Fanfare*: Allegro
II   *Nocturne*: Lento
III   *Chaconne*: Allegro con spirito
Score completed   details unknown
Autograph MS   untraced
First performance   Royal Liverpool Philharmonic Orchestra/Lawrence
   Leonard, Leeds Town Hall, 24 October 1961 (Rostrum Concert)

First London performance   Royal Philharmonic Orchestra/Kenneth Jones,
   Royal Festival Hall, London, 26 March 1962
Publication   Paterson, 1961

Opus 75 constitutes a complete reworking of Divertimento No. 2,
op.24, (**39**), with the central movement retitled *Nocturne*.

GRAND CONCERTO GASTRONOMIQUE
Opus 76   20′00″
for eater, waiter, food and large orchestra
2+picc 2 2 2 – 4 3 3 1 – timp 2perc hp – str
I   *Prologue*: Maestoso – *Oysters* Moderato – Vivace
II   *Soup: Brown Windsor*: Maestoso – Allegro vivace
III   *Roast beef*: Nobilmente
IV   *Cheese*: Maestoso
V   *Peach Melba*: Moderato e molto espressivo
VI   *Coffee, Brandy, Epilogue*: Allegro moderato
Score completed   1 November 1961
Autograph MS   held by the Royal College of Music, London
First performance   Henry Sherek (eater)/Morley College Symphony
   Orchestra/Malcolm Arnold, Royal Festival Hall, London,
   28 November 1961

Grand Concerto Gastronomique was written for the Hoffnung
Astronautical Music Festival.

LEONORA NO. 4 (BEETHOVEN-STRASSER)   9′30″
Overture for orchestra
2+picc 2 2 2 – 4 2 3 1 – timp 2perc – str – 12tpt (offstage) – street band
   (including at least the following): bnjo gtr bd cl cnt *or* tpt trb *or* loud
   bass instrument
Score completed   details unknown
Autograph MS   held by Annetta Hoffnung
First performance   Morley College Symphony Orchestra/Norman del
   Mar, Royal Festival Hall, London, 28 November 1961

Leonora No. 4 was written for the Hoffnung Astronautical Music Festival.

1962

108 CONCERTO FOR TWO VIOLINS AND STRING
ORCHESTRA   Opus 77   16'30"
I   Allegro risoluto
II   Andantino
III Vivace – Presto
Score completed   April 25 1962
Autograph MS   untraced
First performance   Yehudi Menuhin, Albert Lysy (vns)/Bath Festival
  Orchestra/Malcolm Arnold, Guildhall/Bath, 24 June 1962 (Bath Festival)
First London performance   Yehudi Menuhin, Robert Masters (vns)/Bath
  Festival Orchestra/Malcolm Arnold, Victoria and Albert Museum,
  London, 17 June 1964
First broadcast performance   Alfredo Campoli, Derek Collier (vns)/
  London Symphony Orchestra/Malcolm Arnold, BBC Music
  Programme, 28 December 1965 (BBC *Composer's Portrait* series)
Publication   Faber Music, 1966

The Concerto for Two Violins and String Orchestra was commissioned
by Yehudi Menuhin.

109 LITTLE SUITE NO. 2   Opus 78   10'00"
for orchestra
2 2 2 2 – 4 3 3 1 – timp 3perc – str
I   *Overture*: Allegro moderato
II   *Ballad*: Andantino
III *Dance*: Vivace
Score completed   details unknown
Autograph MS   untraced
First performance   combined orchestras of Farnham Grammar School and
  Tiffin School/Dennis Bloodworth, Farnham Parish Church, 13 May
  1963 (Farnham Festival)
First London performance   London Junior and Senior Orchestras/Oliver
  Broome, Royal Festival Hall, London, 25 May 1964
Publication   Paterson, 1963

Little Suite No. 2 was written for the Farnham Festival.

1963

THE PEACOCK IN THE ZOO 2'00"

for unison voices and piano
Text: Katherine Arnold
Allegretto
Score completed   details unknown
Autograph MS   held by Katherine King
Publication   Paterson, 1963

ELECTRA   Opus 79 25'00"

Ballet in one act
2+picc 2 2 2 – 4 3 3 1 – timp 3perc hp – str
Lento – Vivace – Lento – Allegro ma non troppo – Moderato – Vivace –
   Lento
Score completed   Thursley, 13 March 1963
Autograph MS   full score untraced, vocal score (reduction for two
   pianos) held by the Royal College of Music, London
First performance   Orchestra of the Royal Opera House, Covent
   Garden/John Lanchberry/Royal Ballet: Nadia Nerina (Electra), David
   Blair (Orestes), Monica Mason (Clytemnestra), Derek Rencher
   (Aegisthus), David Drew, Christopher Newton, Ronald Plaisted,
   Kenneth Mason, Petrus Bosman, Lambert Cox, David Jones, Austin
   Bennett (The Erinyes)/Robert Helpmann (choreography), Arthur Boyd
   (design), William Bundy (lighting); Royal Opera House, Covent
   Garden, London, 26 March 1963

Electra was commissioned by the Royal Ballet.

LITTLE SUITE NO. 1 FOR BRASS BAND   Opus 80   10'00"

I   *Prelude*: Allegro ma non troppo
II   *Siciliano*: Andantino
III   *Rondo*: Allegro vivace – Presto
Score completed   Thursley, March 1963
Autograph MS   held by E. J. B. Catto (director of the National Youth
   Brass Band of Scotland)
First performance   National Youth Brass Band of Scotland/Bryden

Thomson, High School for Girls, Aberdeen, July 1963
Publication   Paterson, 1965

Little Suite No. 1 for Brass Band was commissioned by the Scottish
Amateur Music Association for the National Youth Brass Band of
Scotland.

112a   Symphonic Band Arrangement: Prelude, Siciliano and Rondo (John
Paynter)

1964

113   W A T E R   M U S I C   Opus 82   10'00"
for wind and percussion
picc 2fl 2ob Ebcl 2cl 2bsn 4hn 3tpt 2ttrb btrb tuba 2perc
I   Allegro maestoso
II   Andantino
III   Vivace
Score completed   details unknown
Autograph MS   untraced
First performance   Ensemble/Brian Priestman, Stratford-upon-Avon,
     11 July 1964
First concert performance   Royal Northern College of Music Wind
     Ensemble/Clark Rundell, BASBWE Conference, RNCM,
     Manchester, 3 November 1984

Water Music was written for the National Trust in celebration of the
opening of the Stratford Canal. It was played, following a performance
of *Henry V*, from a barge moored behind the Shakespeare Memorial
Theatre, at the point where the canal enters the river.

113a   Full Orchestra Arrangement   Opus 82b
2+picc 2 2 2 – 4 3 3 1 – timp 2perc – str
Autograph MS   held by the Royal College of Music, London
First performance   Hallé Orchestra/Lawrence Leonard, Free Trade Hall,
     Manchester, 21 March 1965
Publication   Paterson, 1965

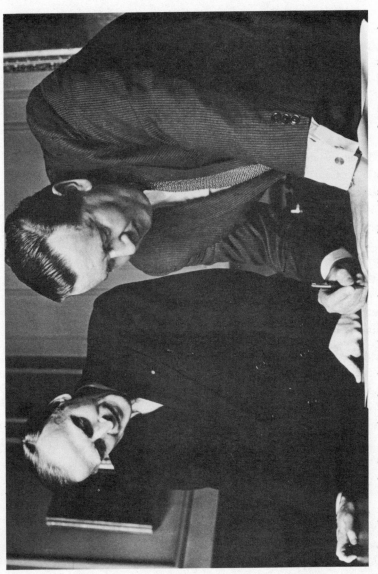

With violinist Yehudi Menuhin after the Bath Festival première of Arnold's Concerto for Two Violins and String Orchestra (1962).

114　A SUNSHINE OVERTURE　Opus 83　　　　　2'00"
　　　for orchestra
　　　2 2 2 2 – 2 2 1 0 – perc – str
　　　Score completed　details unknown
　　　Autograph MS　untraced
　　　First performance　Sunshine Gala Orchestra/Dudley Simpson, Palace
　　　　Theatre, London, 14 July 1964

A Sunshine Overture was written for the Sunshine Home for Blind
Babies.

115　FIVE PIECES FOR VIOLIN AND PIANO　Opus 84　9'00"
　　　I　　*Prelude*: Con energico
　　　II　　*Aubade*: Vivace
　　　III　*Waltz*: Grazioso
　　　IV　*Ballad*: Andantino
　　　V　　*Moto perpetuo*: Presto
　　　Score completed　Thursley, 8 August 1964
　　　Autograph MS　untraced
　　　First performance　Yehudi Menuhin (vn), Ivor Newton (pno), Bamburgh
　　　　Castle, Northumberland, 24 July 1965
　　　First broadcast performance　Derek Collier (vn), Ernest Lush (pno), BBC
　　　　Home Service, 29 January 1966
　　　Publication　Paterson, 1965

The Five Pieces for Violin and Piano were written for Yehudi Menuhin
to use as encore pieces on an American tour. The 'Aubade' is based on an
Indian rāga and the 'Ballad' is derived from the 'Arioso' of *Rinaldo and
Armida* (**68**). The 'Moto perpetuo' is dedicated to Charlie Parker, the jazz
saxophonist.

116　SINFONIETTA NO. 3　Opus 81　　　　　14'30"
　　　for orchestra
　　　1 2 0 2 – 2 0 0 0 – str
　　　I　　Allegro vivace
　　　II　　Vivace
　　　III　Andante con moto
　　　IV　Allegro con energico

Score completed   Thursley, 1 September 1964
Autograph MS   held by the Royal College of Music, London
First performance   New Philharmonia Orchestra/Malcolm Arnold,
   Fairfield Hall, Croydon, 30 January 1965
Publication   Paterson, 1964

1965

DUO FOR TWO CELLOS   Opus 85   5′00″
Allegretto languido
Score completed   5 January 1965
Autograph MS   rough copy only (with original title, 'Serenade'), held by
   the Royal College of Music, London
Publication   Novello, 1971 (in Hugo Cole and Anne Shuttleworth:
   Playing the Cello)

Arrangement for Two Violas (Alison Milne)
Publication   Novello, 1986 (*Playing the Viola*)

Fantasies for Solo Wind Instruments

Arnold was commissioned by the City of Birmingham Symphony
Orchestra to write a set of five Fantasies for the Birmingham
International Wind Competition in May 1966. The first performance of
each Fantasy is, therefore, credited to the winner in the appropriate class.
All autograph MSS are held by the CBSO Library.

FANTASY FOR BASSOON   Opus 86   4′30″
Allegretto – Allegro non troppo – Tempo I – Presto – Lento
Score completed   details unknown
First performance   František Herman, Birmingham Town Hall, May
   1966
Publication   Faber Music, 1966

FANTASY FOR CLARINET   Opus 87   4′30″
Andante con moto – Vivace – Alla marcia – Lento – Tempo I

Score completed   details unknown
First performance   Aurelian–Octav Popa, Birmingham Town Hall, May
  1966
Publication   Faber Music, 1966

120   FANTASY FOR HORN   Opus 88   4'30"
Allegro vivace – Poco lento – Allegro non troppo – Vivace – Lento e
  maestoso – Prestissimo
Score completed   details unknown
First performance   Ferenc Tarjáni, Birmingham Town Hall, May 1966
Publication   Faber Music, 1966

121   FANTASY FOR FLUTE   Opus 89   4'30"
Andante con moto – Vivace e molto ritmico – Allegro marziale – Presto
Score completed   details unknown
First performance   James Galway, Birmingham Town Hall, May 1966
Publication   Faber Music, 1966

122   FANTASY FOR OBOE   Opus 90   4'30"
Allegretto – Vivace – Allegretto – Andante con moto – Presto –
  Allegretto
Score completed   details unknown
First performance   Maurice Bourgue, Birmingham Town Hall,
  May 1966
Publication   Faber Music, 1966

1966

123   FOUR CORNISH DANCES   Opus 91   10'00"
for orchestra
2+picc 2 2 2 – 4 3 3 1 – timp 3perc hp – str
I   Vivace
II   Andantino
III Con moto e sempre senza parodia
IV   Allegro ma non troppo
Score completed   St Merryn, Cornwall, 26 May 1966

Autograph MS held by the Royal College of Music, London
Dedication Isobel Arnold
First performance London Philharmonic Orchestra/Malcolm Arnold,
  Royal Albert Hall, London, 13 August 1966 (Henry Wood
  Promenade Concert)
Publication Faber Music, 1968

Concert Band Arrangement (Thad Marciniak)
Publication Faber Music, 1968, and Schirmer (New York), 1975

Brass Band Arrangement (Ray Farr)
Publication Faber Music, 1985

Arrangement for Orchestra and Brass Band
Note In this arrangement the composer added parts for brass band to
  the original orchestral version in the third and fourth dances only.
Score completed St Merryn, Cornwall, 29 January 1968
Autograph MS held by the Royal College of Music, London
First performance Penzance Orchestral Society, Cornwall Symphony
  Orchestra, St Dennis Silver Band, St Agnes Silver Band/Malcolm
  Arnold, Truro Cathedral, 16 March 1968

THEME AND VARIATION
for orchestra
3 2+ca 2+bcl 0 – 4 3 3 1 – timp 2perc hp – str
Note The Theme and Variation is part of a composite work, *Severn
  Bridge Variations on a Welsh Folk Song* (19'00" duration), written to
  commemorate the opening of the Severn Bridge and the first visit to
  Wales of the BBC Training Orchestra on its first birthday. Arnold
  supplied the theme and first variation. Five more variations were
  composed by Alun Hoddinott, Nicholas Maw, Daniel Jones, Grace
  Williams and Michael Tippett.
Theme: Andante con moto
Variation: Moderato
Score completed October 1966
Autograph MS held by the BBC Music Library (ref. 24805)

First performance BBC Training Orchestra/Sir Adrian Boult, Brangwyn Hall, Swansea, 11 January 1967

First London performance BBC Welsh Symphony Orchestra/Boris Brott, Royal Albert Hall, 20 July 1976 (Henry Wood Promenade Concert)

125 JOLLY OLD FRIAR
for unison voices and piano
Text: Frank Richards
Score completed details unknown
Autograph MS untraced
Publication Cassell, 1966 (*Greyfriars' School Annual*)

1967

126 LITTLE SUITE NO. 2 FOR BRASS BAND Opus 93 8′45″
I   *Round*: Allegro molto e ritmico
II *Cavatina*: Andante con moto
III *Galop*: Presto
Score completed details unknown
Autograph MS untraced
First performance Cornwall Youth Band/Malcolm Arnold, [venue unknown], Easter Sunday, 1967
Publication Henrees Music, 1967

Little Suite No. 2 for Brass Band was commissioned by the Cornwall Youth Band. See also **300**.

126a Military Band Arrangement (Jan Singerling)
Publication Molenaar N.V., 1967

127 THE PADSTOW LIFEBOAT Opus 94 4′30″
March for brass band
Allegro con spirito – Grandioso
Score completed details unknown
Autograph MS untraced
First performance Black Dyke Mills Band, B.M.C. Band/Malcolm

Arnold, Royal Festival Hall, London, 10 June 1967 (BBC International
Festival of Light Music)
First Cornish performance   St Dennis Silver Band/Malcolm Arnold,
Padstow, 19 July 1968
Publication   Henrees Music, 1967

The published score carries the following note: 'The Padstow Lifeboat
has a long and distinguished record. The new lifeboat station is near
Trevose lighthouse whose fog horn varies in pitch between middle C and
D. For the sake of musical unity it remains D throughout this march.'
The first Cornish performance was given on the occasion of the visit of
Princess Marina to name the new lifeboat.

Military Band Arrangement (Ray Woodfield)
Publication   Henrees Music, 1967

SYMPHONY NO. 6   Opus 95   26'00"
for orchestra
2+picc 2 2 2 – 4 3 3 1 – timp 3perc – str
I   Energico
II   Lento
III   Con fuoco
Score completed   St Merryn, Cornwall, 28 July 1967
Autograph MS   untraced
First performance   BBC Northern Symphony Orchestra/Malcolm
Arnold, City Hall, Sheffield, 28 June 1968
First London performance   Royal Philharmonic Orchestra/Malcolm
Arnold, Royal Albert Hall, 24 September 1969
Publication   Faber Music, 1974

TREVELYAN SUITE   Opus 96   8'00"
for ten instruments
3fl 2ob 2cl 2hn vc
Alternative instrumentation   2bsn replace vc
I   *Palindrome*: Allegro spiritoso
II   *Nocturne*: Andante con moto
III   *Apotheosis*: Maestoso

Score completed   St Merryn, Cornwall, 13 October 1967
Autograph MS   untraced
First performance   Ensemble [University of Durham]/Malcolm Arnold,
    Trevelyan College, University of Durham, 12 March 1968
Publication   Faber Music, 1970, and Emerson Edition, 1979

The *Trevelyan Suite* was written for the opening by Lord Butler of
Trevelyan College, University of Durham. Arnold's daughter
Katherine was an undergraduate at the college.

130   THIS CHRISTMAS NIGHT   1'30"
for unaccompanied mixed voices
Text: Mary Wilson
Allegretto
Score completed   details unknown
Autograph MS   untraced
Publication   Faber Music, 1968

131   A SALUTE TO THOMAS MERRITT   Opus 98   5'00"
for two brass bands and orchestra
2+picc 2 2 2 – 4 3 3 1 – timp 4perc hp – str
Maestoso
Score completed   St Merryn, Cornwall, 24 December 1967
Autograph MS   held by the Royal College of Music, London
First performance   St Dennis Silver Band, St Agnes Silver Band,
    Penzance Orchestral Society, Cornwall Symphony
    Orchestra/Malcolm Arnold, Truro Cathedral, 16 March 1968

A Salute to Thomas Merritt was written to celebrate the 60th anniversary
of the death of the Cornish composer Thomas Merritt.

1968

132   PETERLOO   Opus 97   9'45"
Overture for orchestra
2+picc 2 2 2 – 4 3 3 1 – timp 4perc hp – str

Andante con moto – Allegro vivace – Con fuoco – Lento – Andante con
  moto – Maestoso
Score completed   St Merryn, Cornwall, 31 October 1967
Autograph MS   untraced
First performance   Royal Philharmonic Orchestra/Malcolm Arnold,
  Royal Festival Hall, London, 7 June 1968
Publication   Faber Music, 1979

Peterloo was commissioned by the Trades Union Congress for the 100th
anniversary of its first meeting in 1868.

ANNIVERSARY OVERTURE   Opus 99   4′00″
for orchestra
2 2 2 2 – 4 2 3 0 – timp perc – str
Allegro giubiloso
Score completed   St Merryn, Cornwall, 15 July 1968
Autograph MS   untraced
First performance   Hong Kong Philharmonic Orchestra/Arrigo Foa, City
  Hall, Hong Kong, 8 December 1968
First British performance   Orchestra of the Light Music Society/Malcolm
  Arnold, Royal Festival Hall, London, 17 September 1970 (South Bank
  'Pops' concert)
Publication   Faber Music, 1974 (in conjunction with Central Music Library)

Anniversary Overture (originally titled *Hong Kong Anniversary Overture*)
was written for the 21st anniversary of the founding of the Hong Kong
Philharmonic Society.

ST ENDELLION RINGERS   0′30″
Canon for voices
Score completed   details unknown
Autograph MS   held by the Royal College of Music, London

1969

FANTASY FOR TRUMPET   Opus 100   4′00″
Allegro energico – Vivace – Allegretto – Maestoso

Score completed   details unknown
Autograph MS   untraced
Dedication   Ernest Hall
Publication   Faber Music, 1969

Ernest Hall, the dedicatee of the Fantasy for Trumpet, was Arnold's teacher at the Royal College of Music.

136   FANTASY FOR TROMBONE   Opus 101   4'00"
Allegro – Andante – Allegro – Presto
Score completed   details unknown
Autograph MS   untraced
Publication   Faber Music, 1969

137   FANTASY FOR TUBA   Opus 102   4'00"
Grazioso – Allegro – Tempo I – Andante con moto – Tempo I
Score completed   details unknown
Autograph MS   untraced
Publication   Faber Music, 1969

138   THE SONG OF ACCOUNTING PERIODS   Opus 103   2'45"
for voice and piano
Text: from the 1965 Finance Act
Score completed   details unknown
Autograph MS   score untraced, sketch only held by the Royal College of
    Music, London
First performance   John Godber (t), John Gould (pno), Purcell Room,
    London, 4 May 1969

139   CONCERTO FOR 2 PIANOS (3 HANDS) AND
    ORCHESTRA   Opus 104   12'30"
2+picc 2 2 2 – 4 3 3 1 – timp 2perc hp – str
Alternative orchestration   2 2 2 2 – 2 2 1 1 – timp perc – str
I   Allegro moderato
II   Andante con moto
III   Allegro
Score completed   12 June 1969

Autograph MS   untraced
Dedication   'To Phyllis and Cyril with affection and admiration'
First performance   Phyllis Sellick, Cyril Smith (pnos)/BBC Symphony
  Orchestra/Malcolm Arnold, Royal Albert Hall, London, 16 August
  1969 (Henry Wood Promenade Concert)
Publication   Faber Music, 1969

The Concerto for 2 Pianos (3 Hands) and Orchestra was commissioned
by the BBC.

1970

40   CONCERTO FOR 28 PLAYERS   Opus 105   15'00"
1 2 0 1 – 2 0 0 0 – str (6 6 4 4 2)
I   Vivace
II   Larghetto
III   Allegro
Score completed   St Merryn, Cornwall, 2 April 1970
Autograph MS   untraced
First performance   English Chamber Orchestra/Malcolm Arnold, Queen
  Elizabeth Hall, London, 25 April 1970
Publication   Faber Music, 1970

The Concerto for 28 Players was commissioned by the Stuyvesant
Foundation.

41   FANFARE FOR LOUIS   1'30"
for 2 trumpets in Bb
Vivace – Maestoso – Vivace
Score completed   May 1970
Autograph MS   ink score, held by the Royal College of Music, London
Dedication   for 'Louis Armstrong's 70th birthday with admiration and
  gratitude'
First performance   Elgar Howarth, Stanley Woods, Queen Elizabeth
  Hall, London, 4 July 1970 (Louis Armstrong 70th birthday concert)
Publication   Studio Music, 1986

142   FANTASY FOR AUDIENCE AND ORCHESTRA
      Opus 106   13′30″
      2+picc 2 2 2 – 4 3 3 1 – timp 3perc hp org – str
      Allegro non troppo – Vivace – Allegro non troppo – Allegro brillante –
         Allegro non troppo e maestoso – Lento – Allegro moderato e accel. –
      Allegro non troppo – Maestoso – Molto vivace
      Score completed   details unknown
      Autograph MS   held by the BBC Music Library (ref. 25073)
      First performance   BBC Symphony Orchestra/Colin Davis, Royal Albert
         Hall, London, 12 September 1970 (Henry Wood Promenade Concert)

      The Fantasy for Audience and Orchestra was commissioned by the
      BBC.

143   FANTASY FOR GUITAR   Opus 107   10′00″
      Prelude: Maestoso – *Scherzo*: Allegro – *Arietta*: Andante con moto –
         Fughetta – *Arietta*: Semplice e languido – *March*: Allegro – *Postlude*:
         Maestoso
      Score completed   details unknown
      Autograph MS   untraced
      Dedication   Julian Bream
      First performance   Julian Bream, Queen Elizabeth Hall, London, 16 May
         1971
      Publication   Faber Music, 1971

1971

144   CONCERTO FOR VIOLA AND CHAMBER
      ORCHESTRA   Opus 108   20′00″
      1 2 2 2 – 2 0 0 0 – str
      I   Allegro con spirito
      II   Andante con moto
      III   Allegro vivace
      Score completed   St Merryn, Cornwall, 2 March 1971
      Autograph MS   held by the Royal College of Music, London
      Dedication   Roger Best and the Northern Sinfonia

First performance   Roger Best (va)/Northern Sinfonia/Malcolm Arnold,
   Market Hall, Carlisle, 13 October 1971 (Newcastle Festival)
First London performance   Roger Best/Northern Sinfonia/Malcolm
   Arnold, Queen Elizabeth Hall, 15 October 1971
First broadcast performance   Roger Best/Northern Sinfonia/Malcolm
   Arnold, BBC Radio 3, 3 May 1972
Publication   Faber Music, 1980

The Concerto for Viola and Chamber Orchestra was commissioned by
Northern Arts.

1972

POPULAR BIRTHDAY   1′00″
for orchestra
1+2picc 2 2 2 – 4 3 3 1 – timp 2perc hp – str
Maestoso – Moderato
Score completed   St Merryn, Cornwall, February 1972
Autograph MS   held by the BBC Music Library (MS 9021)
Dedication   'for the seventieth birthday of Sir William Walton O.M.,
   with homage and every expression of friendship'
First performance   London Symphony Orchestra/Malcolm Arnold,
   Royal Festival Hall, London, 28 March 1972

Popular Birthday is one of a series of pieces written by various composers
for Walton's 70th birthday concert. It contains a quotation from
Walton's 'Popular Song' (*Façade*).

Reduced Version
fl pno 2perc strqt
Score completed   details unknown
Autograph MS   untraced
First performance   Nash Ensemble/Marcus Dods, BBC Television
   (*Walton at 70*, BBC2), 29 March 1972

SONG OF FREEDOM   Opus 109   19′00″
for chorus of sopranos and altos and brass band

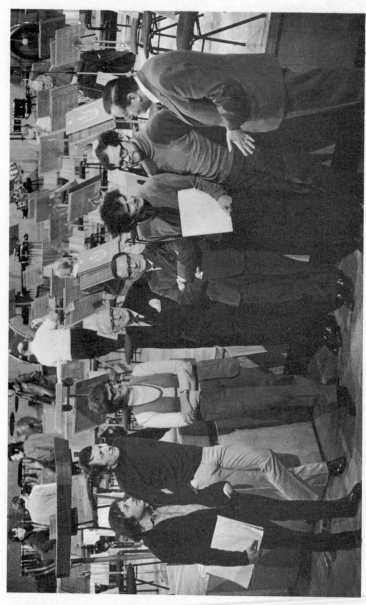

Composers' photo-call at the rehearsal for Walton's 70th birthday concert at the Royal Festival Hall, London. From left to right: André Previn, Richard Rodney Bennett, Thea Musgrave, William Walton, Robert Simpson, Peter Maxwell Davies, Nicholas Maw and Malcolm Arnold (1972).

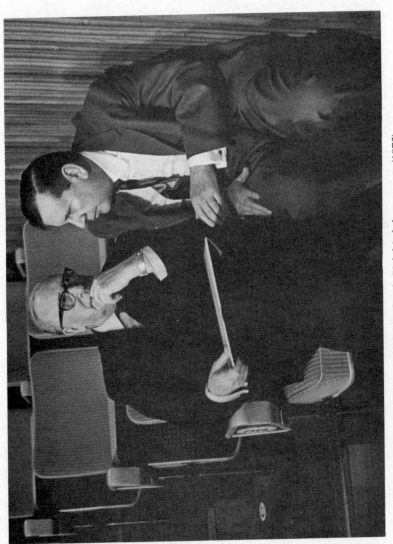

With William Walton at the rehearsal for Walton's 70th birthday concert (1972).

I   *Prelude*: Moderato – Allegro non troppo – Moderato – Allegretto – Moderato – Allegro non troppo – Moderato
    Text: Maureen Parr, Nina Truzka and Susan Selwyn

II   *Hymn*: Risoluto – Allargando
    Text: Vivienne McClean

III   *Intermezzo*: Lento – Blues tempo
    Text: Diana Henry, Caroline Richardson and Marianne Porter

IV   *Postlude*: Maestoso con moto – Allargando
    Text: John Michael Thompson and Maureen Parr

Score completed   details unknown
Autograph MS   untraced
Dedication   the National Schools Brass Band Association, in celebration of the 21st anniversary of its founding
First performance   Netteswell School Band and Choir/Malcolm Arnold, Harlow Sportscentre, 12 May 1973
First London performance   Harrow Schools' Girls Choir/GUS (Footwear) Band/Geoffrey Brand, Royal Albert Hall (National Brass Band Championships of Great Britain Festival), 6 October 1973
Publication   Henrees Music, 1972

Arnold chose the texts for *Song of Freedom* from poems on freedom written by children as part of a nationwide competition sponsored by the NSBBA, who also commissioned the work.

147   THE FAIR FIELD   Opus 110   7'30"
    Overture for orchestra
    2+picc 2 2 2 – 4 3 3 1 – timp 2perc – str
    Vivace – Allegro con brio – Lento e maestoso

Score completed   Dublin, 2 October 1972
Autograph MS   held by the Royal College of Music, London
Dedication   'William Walton with the greatest esteem and affection'
First performance   Royal Philharmonic Orchestra/Malcolm Arnold, Fairfield Hall, Croydon, 27 April 1973
First broadcast performance   BBC Symphony Orchestra/Malcolm Arnold, BBC Radio 3, 16 March 1977
Publication   Faber Music, 1973 (in conjunction with Central Music Library)

The Fair Field was commissioned by Croydon Arts Festival for the 10th anniversary of the opening of the Fairfield Hall.

CONCERTO NO. 2 FOR FLUTE AND ORCHESTRA

Opus 111   14′00″

0 2 0 0 – 2 0 0 0 – str

I   Allegro moderato
II   Vivace
III   Allegretto

Score completed   Dublin, 8 December 1972
Autograph MS   held by Katherine King
Dedication   Richard Adeney
First performance   Richard Adeney (fl)/English Chamber Orchestra/ Kenneth Sillito, The Maltings, Snape, 28 June 1973 (Aldeburgh Festival)
First London performance   Richard Adeney/English Chamber Orchestra/ Wilfried Boettcher, Queen Elizabeth Hall, 1 October 1973
Publication   Faber Music, 1973

1973

A FLOURISH FOR ORCHESTRA   Opus 112   4′00″

2+picc 2 2 2 – 4 3 3 1 – timp 3perc – str

Giubiloso – Allargando

Score completed   Dublin, 11 January 1973
Autograph MS   untraced
First performance   Bournemouth Symphony Orchestra/Rudolf Schwarz, Colston Hall, Bristol, 26 September 1973
Publication   Faber Music, 1973

A Flourish for Orchestra was written to celebrate the 500th anniversary of the granting of the Charter of the City of Bristol.

SYMPHONY NO. 7   Opus 113   45′00″

for orchestra

2+picc 2 2 2+cbsn – 4 3 3 1 – timp 3perc hp – str

I   Allegro energico [Katherine]
II   Andante con moto – Molto vivace – Lento [Robert]
III   Allegro – Allegretto – Allegro – Allegretto – Allegro [Edward]
Score completed   Dublin, 9 September 1973
Autograph MS   untraced
Dedication   the composer's children, Katherine, Robert and Edward, the
  letters of whose names are woven into the musical texture of each
  movement
First performance   New Philharmonia Orchestra/Malcolm Arnold, Royal
  Festival Hall, London, 5 May 1974
First broadcast performance   BBC Symphony Orchestra/Malcolm Arnold,
  BBC Radio 3, 16 March 1977
Publication   Faber Music, 1974

Symphony No. 7 was commissioned by the New Philharmonia
Orchestra.

151   FANTASY FOR BRASS BAND   Opus 114 [a]   10′00″
Prelude: Allegro moderato – *Dance*: Allegretto – *Elegy*: Andante con moto
  – *Scherzo*: Vivace – *Postlude*: Allegro moderato – Vivace
Score completed   details unknown
Autograph MS   untraced
Dedication   Tony Giles
First performance   Cory Band/Major H.A. Kenney, Royal Albert Hall,
  London, 5 October 1974 (National Brass Band Championships)
Publication   Henrees Music, 1974

Fantasy for Brass Band was written for the 1974 National Brass Band
Championships.

1974

152   TWO JOHN DONNE SONGS   Opus 114 [b]   6′00″
for tenor and piano
Note This work and the *Fantasy for Brass Band* (**151**) were both published
  as Opus 114. This was purely accidental, and there is no relationship
  between the two works.

I   *The Good-Morrow*: Andante con moto
II   *Woman's Constancy*: Allegro moderato
Score completed   Dublin, 14 February 1974
Autograph MS   untraced
Dedication   'for Niamh'
First performance   Ian Partridge (t), Jennifer Partridge (pno), Bristol
    University, 23 June 1977
Publication   Roberton, 1977

A sketch exists of the opening bars of a third song, 'The Dreame'.

CONCERTO NO. 2 FOR CLARINET AND ORCHESTRA
Opus 115   17'30"
1+picc 2 0 2 – 2 0 0 0 – timp perc – str
I   Allegro vivace
II   Lento
III   Allegro non troppo – Prestissimo (The Pre-Goodman Rag)
Score completed   Dublin, 24 April 1974
Autograph MS   untraced
Dedication   Benny Goodman, 'with admiration and affection'
First performance   Benny Goodman (cl)/Denver Symphony Orchestra/
    Brian Priestman, Red Rocks, Denver, Colorado, 17 August 1974 (Red
    Rocks Music Festival)
First British performance   Benny Goodman/Park Lane Music Players/
    Malcolm Arnold, St John's Smith Square, London, 11 October 1976
Publication   Faber Music, 1981

Concerto No. 2 for Clarinet and Orchestra was written for Benny
Goodman.

1975

FANTASY ON A THEME OF JOHN FIELD FOR PIANO
AND ORCHESTRA   Opus 116   20'00"
2+picc 2 2 2 – 4 3 3 1 – timp 2perc hp – str
Moderato e molto ritmico – Moderato [piano solo] – Allegro – Vivace –
    Presto – Grazioso – Allegro vivace – Andantino – Allegro vivace –

Lento – *Cadenza* [piano solo] – Maestoso con moto – Vivace
Score completed   Dublin, 17 March 1975
Autograph MS   untraced
Dedication   John Lill
First performance   John Lill (pno)/Royal Philharmonic Orchestra/
   Lawrence Foster, Royal Festival Hall, London, 26 May 1977
Publication   Faber Music, 1975

The theme of the *Fantasy on a Theme of John Field* for Piano and Orchestra is taken from Field's Nocturne in C.

155   RAILWAY FANFARE   1′30″
for 6 fanfare trumpets
Allegro energico
Score completed   7 May 1975
Autograph MS   untraced
First performance   details unknown
Publication   Studio Music, 1986

Railway Fanfare was written for the 150th anniversary of railways in Britain.

156   FANTASY FOR HARP   Opus 117   11′00″
Lament: Maestoso – *March* – *Nocturne*: Andante con moto – *Scherzo*:
   Vivace – *Finale*: Maestoso
Score completed   Dublin, May 1975
Autograph MS   untraced
Dedication   Osian Ellis
First performance   Osian Ellis, Law Society Hall, London, 27 January
   1976
First broadcast performance   Osian Ellis, BBC Radio 3, 8 May 1978
Publication   Faber Music, 1978 (ed. Osian Ellis)

157   STRING QUARTET NO. 2   Opus 118   29′00″
   I   Allegro
   II   Maestoso con molto rubato [solo violin] – Allegro vivace
   III   Andante
   IV   Allegretto – Vivace – Lento

Score completed   Dublin, 12 August 1975
Autograph MS   untraced
Dedication   Hugh Maguire
First performance   Allegri String Quartet: Hugh Maguire, David Roth,
   Patrick Ireland, Bruno Schrecker; Dublin Castle, 9 June 1976
First British performance   Allegri String Quartet, The Maltings, Snape,
   12 June 1976 (Aldeburgh Festival)
Publication   Faber Music, 1976

1976

THE THREE MUSKETEERS
Sketches for a ballet

I   *Academy Theme* ('One for all, all for one'): Maestoso con moto
II   *D'Artagnan*: Allegro
III   *D'Artagnan combined with Academy Theme*: Allegro
IV   *Aramis*: Allegro moderato
V   *La Folia – Dance of Intrigue*: Andante con moto
VI   *Porthos*: Allegro pesante
VII   *Athos*: Allegretto
VIII   *The King*: Marcia pomposo
IX   *M. Bonacieux*: Allegretto
X   *The Cardinal*: Moderato
XI   *Milady*: Andantino
XII   *Buckingham*: Allegro marziale
XIII   *Constance's Sad Dance*: Andante con moto
Autograph MS   piano score, held by the Royal College of Music,
   London

Sketches exist of two further fragments: 'Rochefort' and 'Musketeers'
Dance' (Vivace). the music of 'Constance's Sad Dance' was later
incorporated into the slow movement of the Flute Sonata, op. 121 (**161**).

THE RETURN OF ODYSSEUS   Opus 119   30'00"
Cantata for s a t b chorus and orchestra
Text: Patric Dickinson

2 2 2 2 – 4 3 3 1 – timp 2perc hp – str
Score completed   Dublin, 30 March 1976
Autograph MSS   full score held by the Royal College of Music, London, vocal score untraced
First performance   Schools' Music Association Choirs/Orchestra of the Royal College of Music/Sir David Willcocks, Royal Albert Hall, London, 24 April 1977
Publication   Faber Music, 1976

The Return of Odysseus was commissioned by the Schools' Music Association.

160 PHILHARMONIC CONCERTO   Opus 120   13'00"
for orchestra
2+picc 2+ca 2 2+cbsn – 4 3 3 1 – timp 3perc hp – str
I   *Intrada*: Vivace
II   *Aria*: Andantino
III *Chacony*: Energico
Score completed   Dublin, 23 May 1976
Autograph MS   untraced
First performance   London Philharmonic Orchestra/Bernard Haitink, Royal Festival Hall, London, 31 October 1976
First American performance   London Philharmonic Orchestra/Bernard Haitink, Chicago, 7 November 1976
Publication   Faber Music, 1976

Philharmonic Concerto was commissioned by the Commercial Union Insurance Company for the London Philharmonic Orchestra's bicentennial tour of the USA in 1976.

1977

161 SONATA FOR FLUTE AND PIANO   Opus 121   14'00"
Note   Opus number 121 was also, incorrectly, assigned to Symphony No. 8 (**164**) in the published score of that work.
I   Allegro
II   Andantino

III   Maestoso con molto ritmico – Lento molto – A tempo – Lento
      molto – A tempo – Prestissimo
Score completed   22 January 1977
Autograph MS   held by the Royal College of Music, London
Dedication   James Galway
First performance   James Galway (fl), Anthony Goldstone (pno), The
   New Hall, Cardiff, 19 March 1977 (Cardiff Festival)
First broadcast performance   Richard Adeney (fl), David Johns (pno), BBC
   Radio 3, 19 October 1981
Publication   Faber Music, 1980

The Sonata for Flute and Piano was commissioned by the Welsh Arts
Council.

2   VARIATIONS FOR ORCHESTRA ON A THEME OF
     RUTH GIPPS   Opus 122   13'00"
     1+picc 2 2 2 – 2 2 0 0 – timp – str
Theme: Allegro moderato
I   Vivace
II   Alla marcia
III   Lento
IV   Vivace
V   Allegretto
VI   *Finale*: Maestoso
Score completed   Dun Laoghaire, 22 June 1977
Autograph MS   untraced
First performance   Chanticleer Orchestra/Ruth Gipps, Queen Elizabeth
   Hall, London, 22 February 1978
Publication   Faber Music, 1978

The theme of *Variations for Orchestra on a Theme of Ruth Gipps* is taken
from Ruth Gipps's *Coronation March* of 1953.

1978

163 SYMPHONY FOR BRASS INSTRUMENTS Opus 123

30'30"

picctpt 3tpt hn 3ttrb btrb tuba

I   Allegro moderato – Vivace – Tempo primo
II   Allegretto grazioso
III Andante con moto
IV   Allegro con brio

Score completed London, 9 March 1978
Autograph MS held by the Royal College of Music, London
Dedication 'To Philip Jones on his fiftieth birthday'
First performance Philip Jones Brass Ensemble/Howard Snell,
    Cheltenham Town Hall, 8 July 1979 (Cheltenham Festival)
First London performance Philip Jones Brass Ensemble/Howard Snell,
    Queen Elizabeth Hall, 16 March 1980
Publication Faber Music, 1978

164 SYMPHONY NO. 8 Opus 124

25'00"

for orchestra

Note Symphony No. 8 was published, mistakenly, as Opus 121.
2+picc 2 2 2 – 4 3 3 1 – timp 2perc hp – str

I   Allegro
II   Andantino
III Vivace

Score completed London, 11 November 1978
Autograph MS held by the Royal College of Music, London
First performance Albany Symphony Orchestra/Julius Hegyi, Troy
    Savings Bank Music Hall, Albany, New York, USA, 5 May 1979
First British performance BBC Northern Symphony Orchestra/Sir
    Charles Groves, Royal Northern College of Music, Manchester,
    2 October 1981
First London performance Young Musicians' Symphony Orchestra/James
    Blair, St John's, Smith Square, 26 November 1982
Publication Faber Music, 1981

Symphony No. 8 was commissioned by the Rustam K. Kermani

Foundation in memory of Rustam K. Kermani. The 'pastoral' theme in the first movement is derived from the music for the film *The Reckoning* (**280**).

1982

CONCERTO FOR TRUMPET AND ORCHESTRA
Opus 125   11'30"
2 2 2 2 – 4 2 3 1 – timp 2perc hp – str
I   Allegro energico
II   Andante con moto
III Vivace
Score completed   Northampton, January 1982
Autograph MS   untraced
First performance   John Wallace (tpt)/Royal College of Music Great Gala
   Orchestra/Sir Alexander Gibson, Royal Albert Hall, London,
   30 January 1983
Publication   Faber Music, 1982

The Concerto for Trumpet and Orchestra was commissioned by the Arts Council of Great Britain in celebration of the 100th anniversary of the founding of the Royal College of Music in 1883.

78 autograph scores untraced!

FILM MUSIC

1947

166 A V A L A N C H E P A T R O L   14′00″
Length of film   24′00″
Production   Swiss Avalanche Patrol (GB) – Jack Swain
Director   Jack Swain
Soundtrack   London Symphony Orchestra/John Hollingsworth

167 S E V E N R A F F L A S H E S   8′00″
Length of film   unknown
Production   Cavalier Films
Soundtrack   Orchestra/John Hollingsworth

1948

168 C H A R T I N G T H E S E A S   duration unknown
Length of film   24′00″
Production   unknown
Director   Harold Lowenstein
Soundtrack   Orchestra/John Hollingsworth

169 T W O R A F F L A S H E S   2′00″
Length of film   unknown
Production   Cavalier Films
Soundtrack   Orchestra/John Hollingsworth

GATES OF POWER   11'00"
Alternative title   Stairway to the Sea
Length of film   19'00"
Production   Anglo-Scottish Films
Director   Anthony Squire
Soundtrack   Orchestra/James Walker

HYDROGRAPHY   7'00"
Length of film   unknown
Production   unknown

REPORT ON STEEL   duration unknown
Length of film   10'00"
Production   Data Films for Central Office of Information
Director   Michael Orrom
Soundtrack   Orchestra/John Hollingsworth

See also Symphonic Study: *Machines*, op. 30 (**46**).

BADGER'S GREEN   20'00"
Length of film   62'00"
Production   Highbury Films
Director   John Irwin
Screenplay   R. C. Sherriff
Soundtrack   Orchestra/Muir Mathieson

Arnold's first feature film

MINING REVIEW   duration unknown
Length of film   unknown
Production   Data Films for the Central Office of Information
Director   Michael Orrom
Soundtrack   Orchestra/Malcolm Arnold

METROPOLITAN WATER BOARD   10'00"
Length of film   unknown
Production   World Wide Films
Soundtrack   Orchestra/John Hollingsworth

176 HAWICK, QUEEN OF THE BORDER 7'00"
Length of film unknown
Production Crown Film Unit
Soundtrack Orchestra/John Hollingsworth

177 WOMEN IN OUR TIME 19'03"
Length of film 20'00"
Production This Modern Age
Soundtrack London Symphony Orchestra/Muir Mathieson
Instrumentation 2 1 2+asax 0 – 4 2 2 0 – timp perc pno hp – str(6 4 3 2 1)
 – and women's voices

This was the first of many This Modern Age productions for which
Arnold provided the music. It is probable that Muir Mathieson
conducted them all.

178 COTTON – LANCASHIRE'S TIME FOR
ADVENTURE 20'00"
Length of film 20'00"
Production This Modern Age

179 THE STRUGGLE FOR OIL 20'00"
Length of film 20'00"
Production This Modern Age
Instrumentation 4 2 2+asax 0 – 4 3 3 1 – timp 2perc hp – str

1949

180 EVWs duration unknown
Length of film unknown
Production Data Films for the Central Office of Information
Director Michael Orrom
Soundtrack Orchestra/John Hollingsworth

181 THIS FARMING BUSINESS duration unknown
Length of film unknown
Production Green Park
Soundtrack Orchestra/John Hollingsworth

BRITANNIA MEWS 60'00"
US title The Forbidden Street
Length of film 91'00"
Production Twentieth-Century-Fox (GB) – William Perlberg
Director Jean Negulesco
Screenplay Ring Lardner Jnr from the novel by Margery Sharp
Soundtrack Royal Philharmonic Orchestra/Muir Mathieson

THE FRAZERS OF CABOT COVE duration unknown
Alternative title An Island Story
Length of film 38'00"
Production Green Park
Director Humphrey Swingler
Soundtrack Orchestra/John Hollingsworth

DRUMS FOR A HOLIDAY duration unknown
Length of film 36'00"
Production Anglo-Scottish Films
Director A. R. Taylor
Soundtrack Orchestra/James Walker

TERRA INCOGNITO duration unknown
Length of film 28'00"
Production Verity
Soundtrack Orchestra/Malcolm Arnold

THE BEAUTIFUL COUNTY OF AYR 17'17"
Length of film 18'00"
Production Anglo-Scottish Films
Soundtrack Orchestra/James Walker
Instrumentation 2 1 2 1 – 0 2 2 0 – perc hp – str
Autograph MS full score (7 sections), held by the Royal College of
Music, London

The score is based on arrangements of Robert Burns tunes, one of which
was later used in *Four Scottish Dances*, op. 59 (**81**).

187 FIGHT FOR A FULLER LIFE 20′00″
Length of film 20′00″
Production This Modern Age

188 TRIESTE: PROBLEM CITY 20′00″
Length of film 20′00″
Production This Modern Age

189 DOLLARS AND SENSE 7′00″
Length of film 11′00″
Production Crown Film Unit
Director Diana Pine
Soundtrack Orchestra/John Hollingsworth

190 YOUR WITNESS 25′00″
US title Eye Witness
Length of film 100′00″
Production Warner (GB) – David E. Rose and Joan Harrison
Director Robert Montgomery
Screenplay Hugo Butler, Ian Hunter and William Douglas Home
Soundtrack Orchestra/John Hollingsworth

191 JULIUS CAESAR duration unknown
Length of film unknown
Production Parthian (USA)
Soundtrack Philharmonia Orchestra/Malcolm Arnold

192 ANTHONY AND CLEOPATRA duration unknown
Length of film unknown
Production Parthian (USA)
Soundtrack Philharmonia Orchestra/Malcolm Arnold

193 WHEN YOU WENT AWAY 17′00″
Length of film 20′00″
Production This Modern Age

194 SCIENCE OF THE ORCHESTRA duration unknown
Length of film 35′00″

Production   Realist Films
Director   Alex Strasser
Soundtrack   Orchestra/Muir Mathieson

Follow-up series to Britten's *The Young Person's Guide to the Orchestra*

1950

OIL REVIEW NO. 5   duration unknown
Length of film   unknown
Production   Green Park
Soundtrack   Orchestra/John Hollingsworth

ECA PRODUCTIVITY TEAM   duration unknown
Length of film   unknown
Production   unknown

FIFTY ACRES   duration unknown
Length of film   18'00"
Production   Green Park
Director   Peter Plaskitt
Soundtrack   Orchestra/John Hollingsworth

UP FOR THE CUP   duration unknown
Length of film   76'00"
Production   AB&D Ltd (GB) – Frank Thrower
Director   Jack Raymond
Screenplay   Jack Marks and Con West from an original story by
   Weston and Lee

Percival Mackey composed most of the music, but Arnold scored several
of the longer sequences.

AIRWAYS   duration unknown
Length of film   unknown
Production   John Harvel
Soundtrack   Orchestra/John Hollingsworth

200 THE RIDDLE OF JAPAN 20'26"
Length of film 21'00"
Production This Modern Age
Instrumentation 4 1 1 0 – 4 2 2 0 – timp 2perc pno hp – str (vcs and dbs only)
Autograph MS full score (12 sections) held by the Royal College of Music, London

201 WHERE BRITAIN STANDS duration unknown
Length of film 20'00"
Production This Modern Age

202 THIS IS BRITAIN duration unknown
Length of film unknown
Production Crown Film Unit
Soundtrack Orchestra/John Hollingsworth

203 LET GO FOR'ARD 20'00"
Length of film 20'00"
Production Anglo-American Oil
Soundtrack Orchestra/Malcolm Arnold

1951

204 ALIEN ORDERS duration unknown
Alternative title Malaya
Length of film 11'00"
Production Crown Film Unit for the Central Office of Information
Soundtrack Orchestra/John Hollingsworth

205 NO HIGHWAY duration unknown
US title No Highway in the Sky
Length of film 99'00"
Production Fox (GB) – Louis D. Lighton
Director Henry Koster

Screenplay   R. C. Sherriff, Oscar Millard and Alec Coppel, based on
   the novel by Nevil Shute
Soundtrack   Orchestra/Marcus Dods

HOME TO DANGER   duration unknown
Length of film   66′00″
Production   Lance Comfort
Director   Terence Fisher
Soundtrack   Orchestra/Muir Mathieson

POWER FOR ALL   20′00″
Length of film   20′00″
Production   Wessex Films
Directors   Graham Wallace, Anthony Squire
Soundtrack   Orchestra/Malcolm Arnold

MEN AND MACHINES   duration unknown
Production   Wessex Films
Soundtrack   Orchestra/Malcolm Arnold

WINGS OF DANGER   24′00″
Length of film   73′00″
Production   Exclusive–Lappett (GB) – Anthony Hinds
Director   Terence Fisher
Soundtrack   London Philharmonic Orchestra/Malcolm Arnold

LOCAL NEWSPAPERS   6′00″
Length of film   17′00″
Production   Crown Film Unit
Soundtrack   Orchestra/John Hollingsworth

HOME AT SEVEN   20′00″
US title   Murder on Monday
Length of film   85′00″
Production   London Films (GB) – Maurice Cowan
Director   Ralph Richardson
Screenplay   Anatole de Grunwald from the play by R. C. Sherriff
Soundtrack   Orchestra/Muir Mathieson

1952

212 STOLEN FACE 32'18"
Length of film 72'00"
Production Exclusive Films (GB) – Anthony Hinds
Director Terence Fisher
Screenplay Martin Berkley and Richard H. Lanau
Soundtrack Orchestra/Malcolm Arnold
Instrumentation 3 2 bcl+2 2 – 4 3 3 0 – timp perc hp – str – and solo pno
Autograph MS full score (21 sections), held by the Royal College of
Music, London

213 THE HOLLY AND THE IVY 12'00"
Length of film 83'00"
Production London Films (GB) – Anatole de Grunwald
Director George More O'Ferrall
Screenplay Anatole de Grunwald from the play by Wynyard Browne
Soundtrack Royal Philharmonic Orchestra/Muir Mathieson

214 THE SOUND BARRIER 26'00"
US title Breaking the Sound Barrier
Length of film 118'00"
Production London Films (GB) – David Lean
Director David Lean
Screenplay Terence Rattigan
Soundtrack Royal Philharmonic Orchestra/Muir Mathieson

See also the orchestral rhapsody, *The Sound Barrier*, op. 38 (**54**).

215 CHANNEL ISLANDS 14'00"
Length of film 20'00"
Production British Transport Films
Director Michael Orrom
Soundtrack Orchestra/Malcolm Arnold

216 THE ISLAND 7'00"
Alternative title Kent Oil Refinery
Length of film 25'00"

Production   Data Films
Directors   Peter Pickering, John Ingram
Soundtrack   Orchestra/John Hollingsworth

CURTAIN UP 29′00″
Length of film   85′00″
Production   Constellation (GB) – Robert Garrett
Director   Ralph Smart
Screenplay   Michael Pertwee and Jack Davies from the play
   On Monday Next by Philip King
Soundtrack   Orchestra/Muir Mathieson

THE RINGER 21′00″
Alternative title   Gaunt Stranger
Length of film   78′00″
Production   London Films (GB) – Hugh Perceval
Director   Guy Hamilton
Screenplay   Val Valentine from the novel by Edgar Wallace
Soundtrack   Orchestra/Muir Mathieson

IT STARTED IN PARADISE 37′00″
Length of film   94′00″
Production   British Film Makers (GB) – Leslie Parkyn and
   Sergei Nolbandov
Director   Compton Bennett
Screenplay   Marghanita Laski
Soundtrack   Orchestra/Muir Mathieson
Publication   Song: 'Young Love – A Question of We'
   (words: Marghanita Laski) – Paterson, 1952

FOUR-SIDED TRIANGLE 30′00″
Length of film   74′00″
Production   Exclusive Films (GB) Michael Carreras and Alexander Paul
Director   Terence Fisher
Screenplay   Paul Tabori and Terence Fisher from the novel by
   William F. Temple
Soundtrack   Royal Philharmonic Orchestra/Muir Mathieson

221 INVITATION TO THE DANCE   duration unknown
         Length of film 92'00"
         Production MGM (GB) – Arthur Freed
         Director and Choreographer Gene Kelly
         Soundtrack Orchestra/John Hollingsworth

Written in collaboration with Jacques Ibert

1953

222 GILBERT AND SULLIVAN   duration unknown
         Length of film unknown
         Production London Films
         Soundtrack Orchestra/Sir Malcolm Sargent

Arrangements of Sullivan tunes

223 THE CAPTAIN'S PARADISE   50'00"
         Alternative title Paradise
         Length of film 89'00"
         Production London Films (GB) – Anthony Kimmins
         Director Anthony Kimmins
         Screenplay Alec Coppell and Nicholas Phipps
         Soundtrack Orchestra/Muir Mathieson
         Instrumentation 1 1 2 1 – 3 2 2 0 – timp 2perc gtr pno hp – str
         Autograph MS full score (opening titles and piano solo 'Flamenco'
            only), held by the Royal College of Music, London

224 MAN OF AFRICA   duration unknown
         Alternative title Kigusi Story
         Length of film 74'00"
         Production Group Three (GB) – John Grierson
         Director Cyril Frankel
         Screenplay Montagu Slater
         Soundtrack Orchestra/Malcolm Arnold

COPENHAGEN, CITY OF TOWERS 12'00"
Length of film   unknown
Production   Fitzpatrick Traveltalk

ALBERT RN duration unknown
Alternative title   Spare Man
US title   Break to Freedom
Length of film   88'00"
Production   Dial (GB) – Daniel M. Angel
Director   Lewis Gilbert
Screenplay   Guy Morgan and Vernon Harris from the play by
   Guy Morgan and Edward Sammis
Soundtrack   Orchestra/Philip Martel

YOU KNOW WHAT SAILORS ARE 45'00"
Length of film   89'00"
Production   Julian Wintle (GB) – Peter Rogers
Director   Ken Annakin
Screenplay   Peter Rogers
Soundtrack   Orchestra/Muir Mathieson
Instrumentation   3 2 2 1 – 4 3 3 1 – timp 2perc hp – str, and in Dance Band
   sequence: 2asax 2tsax 4tpt 4trb gtr drums pno db
Autograph MS   full score (35 sections), held by the Royal College of
   Music, London

POWERED FLIGHT: THE STORY OF THE
CENTURY 38'00"
Length of film   54'00"
Production   Shell Film Unit (GB) – Stuart Legg
Soundtrack   Orchestra/Malcolm Arnold

Documentary based on original research for the Royal Aeronautical
Society by Adrian de Potier

DEVIL ON HORSEBACK 50'00"
Length of film   unknown
Length of film   unknown

Production   Group Three
Director   Cyril Frankel
Soundtrack   Orchestra/Malcolm Arnold

The story of Lester Piggott, the jockey

230   HOBSON'S CHOICE   duration unknown
Length of film   107'00"
Production   London Films (GB) – Norman Spencer
Director   David Lean
Screenplay   Norman Spencer and Wynyard Browne from the play by
   Harold Brighouse
Soundtrack   Royal Philharmonic Orchestra/Muir Matheson
Publication   'Souvenir Selection', 'The Hobson's Choice Theme' and
   'The Willie Mossop Theme' (words: Ginette Bozec) (arr Tony Fones),
   Paterson, 1954

1954

231   THE ROYAL TOUR – NEW ZEALAND   25'00"
Length of film   29'00"
Production   Pathé Documentary Unit (GB) – Howard Thomas
Soundtrack   Orchestra/Muir Matheson

232   THE SLEEPING TIGER   35'00"
Length of film   89'00"
Production   Insignia (GB) – Victor Hanbury
Director   Joseph Losey
Screenplay   Harold Buchman and Carl Foreman from the novel by
   Maurice Moiseiwitch
Soundtrack   Orchestra/Muir Matheson

233   WELCOME THE QUEEN   21'00"
Length of film   50'00"
Production   Pathé Documentary Unit
Soundtrack   Orchestra/Muir Matheson

4 BEAUTIFUL STRANGER duration unknown
US title Twist of Fate
Length of film 89'00"
Production Maxwell Setton and John R. Sloan
Director David Miller
Screenplay Robert Westerby and Carl Nystrom
Soundtrack Orchestra/Malcolm Arnold

5 THE BELLES OF ST TRINIAN'S 25'18"
Length of film 91'00"
Production London Films (GB) – Frank Launder and Sidney Gilliat
Director Frank Launder
Screenplay Frank Launder, Sidney Gilliat and Val Valentine
Soundtrack Orchestra/Malcolm Arnold
Instrumentation 1 1 1 1 – 0 2 1 0 – 2perc pno duet – str (opening titles: 4perc 2pnos)
Autograph MS full score (35 sections) and 'The St Trinian's School Song' for unison voices and piano, held by the Royal College of Music, London

6 THE SEA SHALL NOT HAVE THEM 26'00"
Length of film 93'00"
Production Eros (GB) – Daniel M. Angel
Director Lewis Gilbert
Screenplay Lewis Gilbert and Vernon Harris
Soundtrack Orchestra/Muir Mathieson

7 THE CONSTANT HUSBAND 24'00"
Length of film 88'00"
Production London Films (GB) – Frank Launder and Sidney Gilliat
Director Sidney Gilliat
Screenplay Sidney Gilliat and Val Valentine
Soundtrack London Philharmonic Orchestra/Muir Mathieson

8 A PRIZE OF GOLD 30'00"
Length of film 100'00"
Production Warwick (GB) – Phil C. Samuel

Working on the score for *A Prize of Gold* (1954).

Director   Mark Robson
Screenplay   Robert Buckner and John Paxton from the novel by
   Max Catto
Soundtrack   Orchestra/Muir Mathieson

1955

THE NIGHT MY NUMBER CAME UP 20'00"
Length of film   94'00"
Production   Ealing Studios (GB) – Tom Morahan
Director   Leslie Norman
Screenplay   R. C. Sherriff
Soundtrack   London Symphony Orchestra/Muir Mathieson

I AM A CAMERA 23'00"
Length of film   99'00"
Production   Romulus (GB) – Jack Clayton
Director   Henry Cornelius
Screenplay   John Collier
Soundtrack   Orchestra/Muir Mathieson

VALUE FOR MONEY 30'00"
Length of film   93'00"
Production   Group Films (GB) – Sergei Nolbandov
Director   Ken Annakin
Screenplay   R. F. Delderfield and William Fairchild from the novel by
   Derrick Boothroyd
Soundtrack   Orchestra/Muir Mathieson

THE DEEP BLUE SEA 24'00"
Length of film   99'00"
Production   London Films (GB) – Anatole Litvak
Director   Anatole Litvak
Screenplay   Terence Rattigan
Soundtrack   Orchestra/Muir Mathieson

243 THE WOMAN FOR JOE   30'00"
Length of film   91'00"
Production   Rank (GB) – Leslie Parkyn
Director   George More O'Ferrall
Screenplay   Neil Paterson
Soundtrack   Orchestra/Muir Mathieson

244 1984   35'00"
Length of film   91'00"
Production   Holliday (GB) – N. Peter Rathvon
Director   Michael Anderson
Screenplay   William P. Templeton and Ralph Bettinson from the novel
   by George Orwell
Soundtrack   London Symphony Orchestra/Louis Levy

1956

245 PORT AFRIQUE   29'00"
Length of film   unknown
Production   David E. Rose (GB) – John R. Sloan
Director   Rudolph Maté
Screenplay   Frank Patos and John Cresswell from the novel by
   Bernard Vieter Dryer
Soundtrack   Orchestra/Muir Mathieson

246 TRAPEZE   59'00"
Length of film   105'00"
Production   Hecht-Lancaster (USA) – James Hill
Director   Carol Reed
Screenplay   James R. Webb
Soundtrack   Orchestra/Muir Mathieson
Publication   'Lola's Theme' (words: Al Stillman) – Cromwell Music and
   Essex Music, 1956

247 A HILL IN KOREA   20'00"
US title   Hell in Korea

Length of Film   81′00″
Production   Wessex (GB) – Anthony Squire
Director   Julian Amyes
Screenplay   Ian Dalrymple, Anthony Squire and Ronald Spencer from
   the novel by Max Catto
Soundtrack   Orchestra/Muir Mathieson

48   WICKED AS THEY COME   37′00″
US title   Portrait in Smoke
Length of film   94′00″
Production   Film Locations (GB) – Maxwell Setton
Director   Ken Hughes
Screenplay   Ken Hughes, Robert Westerby and Sigmund Miller
Soundtrack   Sinfonia of London/Muir Mathieson

49   THE BARRETTS OF WIMPOLE STREET   duration unknown

Arnold provided the original score and conducted his own music for the
film. However this was replaced by music by Bronislau Kaper when the
film was released.

50   TIGER IN THE SMOKE   14′00″
Length of film   94′00″
Production   Rank (GB) – Leslie Parkyn
Director   Roy Baker
Screenplay   Anthony Pelissier from the novel by Marjorie Allingham
Soundtrack   Orchestra/Malcolm Arnold

51   ROSES TATTOO   duration unknown
Length of film   unknown
Production   Anglo-Scottish Pictures
Soundtrack   Orchestra/James Walker

1957

252   ISLAND IN THE SUN   28′30″
Length of film   119′00″
Production   Twentieth-Century-Fox (GB) – Darryl F. Zanuck
Director   Robert Rossen
Screenplay   Alfred Hayes from the novel by Alec Waugh
Soundtrack   Royal Philharmonic Orchestra/Malcolm Arnold
Publication   Themes (arr piano solo by Cecil Bolton) – Robbins Music
    Corp., 1957

253   BLUE MURDER AT ST TRINIAN'S   30′30″
Length of film   86′00″
Production   Vale (GB) – Sidney Gilliat and Frank Launder
Director   Frank Launder
Screenplay   Frank Launder, Val Valentine and Sidney Gilliat
Soundtrack   Orchestra/Malcolm Arnold

254   THE BRIDGE ON THE RIVER KWAI   34′00″
Length of film   161′00″
Production   Horizon (GB) – Sam Spiegl
Director   David Lean
Screenplay   Carl Foreman from the novel by Pierre Boulle
Soundtrack   Royal Philharmonic Orchestra/Malcolm Arnold

(i)   *River Kwai Album*   'Title Music', 'River Kwai March', 'Shear's
    Escape', 'Nicholson's Victory', 'Working on the Bridge', 'Trek to
    the Bridge', 'Camp Concert Dance', Camp Concert Song: 'I give
    my heart to no one but you' (words: Dave Shand), 'Finale'
    Publication   Columbia Pictures Music Corp., New York, and
    Campbell Connelly, London, 1958
(ii)   'The River Kwai March' (arr Robert C. Haring for piano solo)
    Publication   Columbia Pictures Music Corp., New York, and
    Campbell Connelly, London, 1957
(iii)   'The River Kwai March' (arr G. Green)
    Instrumentation   2 2 2 2 – 4 2 3 0 – timp perc hp – str
    Publication   Campbell Connelly, London

In Arnold's Drawing Room at 12 Denby Gardens, Richmond, Surrey. On his left is the Oscar he was awarded for his music for *The Bridge On the River Kwai* (1957).

(iv)   'The River Kwai March' (arr Gilbert Vinter for military band)
       Publication   Campbell Connelly, London

Other arrangement   'River Kwai Patrol' (arr R. Berry for military band –
an adaptation of Alford's 'Colonel Bogey' and themes from the film)

255   DUNKIRK   26'00"
Length of film   135'00"
Production   Ealing Studios (GB) – Michael Balcon
Director   Leslie Norman
Screenplay   W. P. Lipscomb and David Divine
Soundtrack   Sinfonia of London/Muir Mathieson

1958

256   THE KEY   50'00"
Length of film   134'00"
Production   Open Road (GB) – Carl Foreman
Director   Carol Reed
Screenplay   Carl Foreman from the novel *Stella* by Jan de Hartog
Soundtrack   Orchestra/Malcolm Arnold
Publication   Title Song/'Stella' (words: Al Stillman) and 'Chop Suey
   Polka' (piano solo) – Columbia Pictures Music Corp., and Campbell
   Connelly, 1958

257   THE ROOTS OF HEAVEN   32'00"
Length of film   125'00"
Production   Twentieth-Century-Fox (GB) – Darryl F. Zanuck
Director   John Huston
Screenplay   Romain Gary and Patrick Leigh-Fermor from the novel by
   Romain Gary
Soundtrack   Orchestra/Malcolm Arnold
Instrumentation   2 2 2 cbsn+1 – 4 3 3 1 – timp perc pno hp – str (8 7 6 5 4)
Autograph MS   overture only, held by the Royal College of Music,
   London

THE INN OF THE SIXTH HAPPINESS 62'30"

Length of film 158'00"
Production Twentieth-Century-Fox (GB) – Mark Robson
Director Mark Robson
Screenplay Isobel Lennart from the book *The Small Woman* by
  Alan Burgess
Soundtrack Royal Philharmonic Orchestra/Malcolm Arnold
Instrumentation 0 1 0 0 – 1 0 0 0 – gtr 2perc cel hp – str

(i) Title song (words: Paul Francis Webster)
  Publication B. Feldman & Co., 1958
(ii) Title song (Swedish text: Gosta Rybrant)
  Publication Reuter and Reuter Forlass AB, 1958
(iii) Theme for piano solo
  Publication B. Feldman & Co., 1958
(iv) 'This Old Man' (from an original arr by Cecil Sharp and
  Baring Gould)
  Publication B. Feldman & Co., 1958
(v) 'This Old Man' (Swedish text: 'Ninita')
  Publication Reuter and Reuter Forlass AB, 1958
(vi) 'This Old Man' (arr)
  Instrumentation 2 2 2 2 – 2 2 3 0 – timp perc hp gtr pno – str
  Publication B. Feldman & Co.
(vii) Selection arr E. Giebert for brass band
  Publication B. Feldman & Co., 1961

An arrangement by Rodney Bashford of the 'Children's March' for
military band has been recorded.

COUPE DES ALPES duration unknown

Length of film 35'00"
Production Shell Film Unit
Director John Armstrong
Soundtrack Orchestra/Malcolm Arnold

1959

260 THE BOY AND THE BRIDGE   42′00″
Length of film   91′00″
Production   Xanadu (GB) – Kevin McClory
Director   Kevin McClory
Screenplay   Geoffrey Orme, Kevin McClory and Desmond O'Donovan
Soundtrack   Orchestra/Malcolm Arnold

261 SOLOMON AND SHEBA   duration unknown
Length of film   142′00″
Production   United Artists (USA) – Ted Richmond
Director   King Vidor
Screenplay   Anthony Veiller, Paul Dudley and George Bruce

Though Mario Nascimbene is credited with the entire score,
Malcolm Arnold wrote the 'Funeral Music' sequence.

262 SUDDENLY LAST SUMMER   48′30″
Length of film   114′00″
Production   Horizon (USA) – Sam Spiegl
Director   Joseph L. Mankiewicz
Screenplay   Gore Vidal from the play by Tennessee Williams
Soundtrack   Orchestra/Buxton Orr (who collaborated on the score)
Autograph MS   piano score (title theme only), held by the Royal College
   of Music, London

1960

263 THE ANGRY SILENCE   7′30″
Length of film   94′00″
Production   Beaver (GB) – Richard Attenborough and Bryan Forbes
Director   Guy Green
Screenplay   Bryan Forbes
Soundtrack   Orchestra/Malcolm Arnold

4 TUNES OF GLORY   7'00"
Length of film   107'00"
Production   Knightsbridge (GB) – Albert Fennell and Colin Lesslie
Director   Ronald Neame
Screenplay   James Kennaway from his novel
Soundtrack   Orchestra/Malcolm Arnold
Instrumentation   picc+1 1 bcl+3 0 – 4 3 3 1 – timp 2perc hp pn – str (vcs
   dbs)

(i)   'The Black Bear' (arr piano solo)
      Publication   United Artists Music Ltd, 1960
(ii) 'Tunes of Glory' theme (words: Mel Mandel and Norman Sachs)
      Publication   United Artists Music Ltd, 1961

5 THE PURE HELL OF ST TRINIAN'S   32'30"
Length of film   94'00"
Production   Vale (GB) – Sidney Gilliat and Frank Launder
Director   Frank Launder
Screenplay   Frank Launder, Val Valentine and Sidney Gilliat
Soundtrack   Orchestra/Malcolm Arnold

6 NO LOVE FOR JOHNNIE   35'00"
Length of film   111'00"
Production   Five Star (GB) – Betty E. Box
Director   Ralph Thomas
Screenplay   Nicholas Phipps and Mordecai Richler from the novel by
   Wilfred Fienburgh
Soundtrack   Orchestra/Malcolm Arnold
Publication   Theme (words: Leslie Bricusse) and 'To the Hustings'
   (orchestra) – Film Music Publishing, 1961

1961

67 WHISTLE DOWN THE WIND   35'00"
Length of film   99'00"
Production   Allied Film Makers/Beaver (GB) – Richard Attenborough

Director   Bryan Forbes
Screenplay   Keith Waterhouse and Willis Hall from the novel by
    Mary Hayley Bell
Soundtrack   Orchestra/Malcolm Arnold

(i)   Theme (piano solo)
    Publication   Henrees Music, 1961
(ii)   Theme (arr J. Arthey)
    Instrumentation   2 1 2 0 – 2 2 2 0 – perc cel gtr – str
    Publication   B. Feldman & Co.

268   ON THE FIDDLE   14′00″
US title   Operation Snafu
Length of film   97′00″
Production   Anglo-Amalgamated (GB) – S. Benjamin Fisz
Director   Cyril Frankel
Screenplay   Harold Buchman from the novel *Stop at a Winner* by
    R. F. Delderfield
Soundtrack   Orchestra/Malcolm Arnold
Publication   Theme (piano solo) – Henrees Music, 1961

1962

269   THE INSPECTOR   51′00″
US title   Lisa
Length of film   111′00″
Production   Twentieth-Century-Fox (GB) – Mark Robson
Director   Philip Dunne
Screenplay   Nelson Gidding from the novel by Jan de Hartog
Soundtrack   Orchestra/Malcolm Arnold

(i)   'Lisa's Theme' (piano solo)
    Publication   Henrees Music, 1962, Francis-Day Muziekuitgevers
        NV, 1962 and Canciones Francis-Day, 1962
(ii)   Theme (arr K. Papworth)
    Instrumentation   2 2 2 2 – 4 3 3 0 – timp perc hp pno – str
    Publication   Henrees Music

THE LION
duration unknown

Length of film 96'00"
Production Twentieth-Century-Fox (GB) – Samuel C. Engel
Director Jack Cardiff
Screenplay Irene and Louis Kamp from the novel by Joseph Kessel
Soundtrack Orchestra/Malcolm Arnold
Publication Theme (piano solo) – Henrees Music, 1962

NINE HOURS TO RAMA
duration unknown

Length of film 125'00"
Production Twentieth-Century-Fox/Red Lion (GB) – Mark Robson
Director Mark Robson
Screenplay Nelson Gidding from the novel by Stanley Wolpert
Soundtrack Orchestra/Malcolm Arnold
Publication Theme (piano solo) – Henrees Music, 1963

1963

TAMAHINE
70'26"

Length of film 95'00"
Production ABP (GB) – John Bryan
Director Philip Leacock
Screenplay Dennis Cannan from the novel by Thelma Niklaus
Soundtrack Orchestra/Malcolm Arnold
Instrumentation 1 1 2+bcl 0 – 3 2 1 0 – Hawaiian gtr+2 3perc cel hp – str, and for the Concert Band Sequence, including the 'Royal Fireworks Music' – picc ob Ebcl 3cl 2bsn 4hn 2tpt 3trb euph tuba perc
Autograph MS full score (29 sections) and vocal score extracts ('Hallow School Song', 'Hallow Cricket Song' and 'Never Forget Boys', held by the Royal College of Music, London
Publication Theme only – Harms Witmark, London, 1963

THE CHALK GARDEN
duration unknown

Length of film 106'00"
Production Quota Rentals (GB) – Ross Hunter
Director Ronald Neame

Screenplay   John Michael Hayes from the novel by Enid Bagnold
Soundtrack   Orchestra/Malcolm Arnold
Publication   'Madrigal Theme' (piano solo) and 'Madrigal' (words: Mack
   David) – Henrees Music, 1964, and Editions Feldman SA, 1964, as
   'Ton Souvenir' (French words: Hubert Ithier)

1964

274   THE THIN RED LINE   duration unknown
   Length of film   99'00"
   Production   ACE (US) – Sidney Harmon
   Director   Andrew Marton
   Screenplay   Bernard Gordon from the novel by James Jones
   Soundtrack   Orchestra/Malcolm Arnold

1966

275   THE HEROES OF TELEMARK   55'00"
   Length of film   131'00"
   Production   Benton (GB) – Ben Fisz
   Director   Anthony Mann
   Screenplay   Ivan Moffat and Ben Barzman
   Soundtrack   Orchestra/Malcolm Arnold
   Publication   'Anna (Love Theme)' and Main Title, piano solo and arr
      orchestra – Screen Gems – Columbia Pictures Music Corp., 1966

276   SKY WEST AND CROOKED   duration unknown
   US title   Gypsy Girl
   Length of film   102'00"
   Production   John Mills (GB)
   Director   John Mills
   Screenplay   Mary Hayley Bell and John Prebble
   Soundtrack   Orchestra/Malcolm Arnold
   Publication   Theme (arr piano solo) – Henrees Music, 1966

THE GREAT ST TRINIAN'S TRAIN ROBBERY
duration unknown

Length of film   unknown
Production   Frank Launder and Sidney Gilliat (GB) – Leslie Gilliat
Directors   Frank Launder and Sidney Gilliat
Screenplay   Frank Launder and Ivor Herbert
Soundtrack   Orchestra/Malcolm Arnold (including 'Ballad of the Great Train Robbery')

AFRICA – TEXAS STYLE
30'00"

US title   Cowboy in Africa
Length of film   109'00"
Production   Vantors (GB) – Andrew Marton
Director   Andrew Marton
Screenplay   Andy White
Soundtrack   Orchestra/Malcolm Arnold

1967

NORTH SEA STRIKE
15'00"

Length of film   20'00"
Production   Gerald Holdsworth Productions
Director   Don Kelly
Soundtrack   Orchestra/Malcolm Arnold

1969

THE RECKONING
30'00"

Alternative title   A Matter of Honour
Length of film   108'00"
Production   Ronald Shedlo (GB) – Hugh Perceval
Director   Jack Gold
Screenplay   John McGrath from the novel *The Harp that Once* by Patrick Hall
Soundtrack   Orchestra/Malcolm Arnold

Publication   Piano selection (Title Theme (Moderato); 'Believe me if all those endearing young charms', arr; 'Piano theme at Party' (slow Foxtrot); 'Ireland's Enemy' (March) – Screen Gems – Columbia Pictures Music Corp., 1969

281   THE BATTLE OF BRITAIN   12'00"
Length of film   131'00"
Production   United Artists (GB) – Harry Saltzman and Ben Fisz
Director   Guy Hamilton
Screenplay   James Kennaway and Wilfrid Greatorex
Soundtrack   Orchestra/Malcolm Arnold and William Walton (for the March)
Instrumentation   picc+2 ca+2 bcl+2 cbsn+2 – 4 3 3 1 – timp 3perc hp – str
Autograph MS   held by Oxford University Press and United Artists Music

Arnold conducted the majority of the sessions during the recording of the soundtrack and assisted in orchestrating several sections of the music, including the 'Battle of Britain March' from Walton's 3-stave short score. Later, when more music was required by the film company, he both rescored and expanded several sections of Walton's original soundtrack including the famous 'Battle in the Air' sequence, the last third of which he completed. At the last minute Walton's soundtrack was replaced by a new score by Ron Goodwin, with the exception of the 'Battle in the Air' sequence which could not be removed because the film was already edited to the music.

The scores in Arnold's hand are:
5M1 – 'Pilot's Run' (Vivace) – 0'59"
12M1 – 'Interior of Heinkel' (Vivace) – 1'15"
13M1 – 'Battle in the Air' – pp. 1–15 in Walton's hand, pp. 16–24 in Arnold's – 5'08"
14M1 and 14M2 – marked 'suspense quiet and insistent throughout' – 1'31"
14M3 – (Allegro) leading to 'Battle of Britain March' – 2'14"
14M3A – alternative introduction to 14M3 – 2'11"
'Horst Wessel Song' (Alla Marcia) – 1'27"

2   DAVID COPPERFIELD   45′00″
Length of film   118′00″
Production   Omnibus/Biography (GB) – Frederick Brogger
Director   Delbert Mann
Screenplay   Jack Pulman based on the novel by Charles Dickens
Soundtrack   Orchestra/Malcolm Arnold
Publication   Twentieth Century Music Corporation, 1970

1980

3   THE WILDCATS OF ST TRINIAN'S   duration unknown
Length of film   91′00″
Production   Wildcat Film Productions (GB) – E. M. Smedley-Aston
Director   Frank Launder
Screenplay   Frank Launder

Music composed by James Kenelm Clarke, with music by Malcolm
Arnold from earlier St Trinian's films, ('School Song', 'The Charge of
the Fourth Form', 'End Titles', 'St Trinian's March')

INCIDENTAL MUSIC FOR RADIO, TELEVISION AND THEATRE

1953

284 PURPLE DUST   duration unknown
Incidental music for the play
Written by   Sean O'Casey
Producer   Sam Wanamaker
Instrumentation   fl hp perc strqt
Autograph MS   held by Eileen O'Casey
First performance   Theatre Royal, Glasgow, April 1953

Arrangements of Irish folk songs

1954

285 THE TEMPEST   duration unknown
Incidental music for the play
Written by   William Shakespeare
Producer   Robert Helpmann
Costumes and décor   Leslie Hurry
Music   in 35 sections including:
   Ariel's Songs:
   (i)   Come unto these yellow sands
   (ii)   Full fathom five thy father lies
   (iii)   While you here do snoring lie
   (iv)   Where the bee sucks
   Juno's Song:
   (v)   Honour, riches, marriage, blessing
Instrumentation   ob cl tpt trb hp glsp cel or vib timp perc
Autograph MS   score, and separate vocal score of (iv), held by the Royal
   College of Music, London

Music played by   Old Vic Theatre Orchestra/Christopher Whelan
First performance   Old Vic Theatre, London, 13 April 1954
Publication   Paterson, 1959 (Three Songs for unison voices and piano –
   Lyric Collection No. 1763)

PADDY'S NIGHTMARE   duration unknown
Revue number written for the Laurier Lister entertainment, *Joyce Grenfell
   Requests the Pleasure*
Instrumentation   vn va vc db cl/sax tr drums pno
Autograph MS   untraced
First performance   Paddy Stone (who devised and arranged the dance
   number) with Theatre Orchestra/William Blezard, Fortune Theatre,
   London, 2 June 1954

WAR IN THE AIR   duration unknown
Music for the BBC TV series
(i)   'The Fated Sky' – televised 8 November 1954 (recorded
         12/13 October)
(ii)   'Maximum Effort' – televised 29 November 1954
(iii)   'Operation Overlord' – televised 10 January 1955
Written and produced by   John Elliot
Series Director   Philip Doreté
Instrumentation   (for 'The Fated Sky') 2 1 2 1 – 4 3 3 1 – timp perc – str
Autograph MS   full score of 'The Fated Sky' only (12 sections), held by
   the BBC Music Library (MS 1383)
Soundtrack   London Symphony Orchestra/Muir Mathieson

1955

CANDLEMAS NIGHT   15′00″
A fantastic comedy
Incidental music for the radio play
Length of play   105′00″
Written by   Ernest Reynolds
Producer   Frederick Bradnum
Instrumentation   picc 2fl tpt timp perc hp cel

Autograph MS   full score (15 sections), held by the BBC Music Library
   (Ref. MS 31082)
Music played by   Chamber Ensemble/Lionel Salter (recorded
   18 November 1955)
Broadcast date   BBC Third Programme, 25 December 1955

289   ELECTRA   6'00"
Incidental music for the play
Written by   Sophocles
Producers   Thomas Vaughan and Donald Bisset
Music
   I   *Prelude*: Poco lento e espressivo
   II   *Electra's Entrance*: Andantino ma agitato
   III   Lento alla marcia funerale
   IV   Lento e misterioso
   V   *Postlude*: Moderato ma non troppo allegro
Instrumentation   fl and perc (cym t–t glsp or pno with sustaining pedal)
Autograph MS   held by the Royal College of Music, London
Music played by   Christopher Hyde-Smith (fl) and James Wolfenden
   (perc)
First performance   Borough Polytechnic Players, Edric Hall, Borough
   Polytechnic, London, 7 December 1955

1956

290   FANFARE   1'30"
Titles for ABC Television
Written for the launch of the ABC Television Network
Music played by   Orchestra/Muir Mathieson

1957

291   FOR MR PYE AN ISLAND   12'00"
Music for the radio play

Length of play   60'00"
Written by   Mervyn Peake (based on incidents from his novel *Mr Pye*)
Producer   Francis Dillon
Instrumentation   2fl cl bcl tpt perc hp pno cel db
Autograph MS   full score (38 sections with cues), held by the
   Royal College of Music, London
Music played by   Chamber Ensemble/Malcolm Arnold
Broadcast date   BBC Home Service, 10 July 1957

ROYAL PROLOGUE   21'00"
Music for television
Length of programme   31'00"
Written by   Christopher Hassall
Producer   Rex Moorfoot
Instrumentation   1 1 2 0 – 1 2 1 0 – timp perc hp pno – str
Autograph MS   full score (17 sections), held by the BBC Music Library
   (MS 2394) and organ solo, held by the Royal College of Music, London
Music played by   Royal Philharmonic Orchestra/Malcolm Arnold; and in
   the Westminster Abbey sequence:
   (i)   Fanfare – by Trumpeters of the Royal Military School of Music,
         Kneller Hall/Lt.-Col. David McBain
   (ii) Organ Solo: Poco lento – by Sir William McKie
   Transmission date   25 December 1957 in programme *Christmas Round
      The World* (see **87**)

1959

MUSIC FOR YOU   2'30"
Signature tune for the BBC TV series, 1959–61
Vivace – Allegretto
Instrumentation   picc+2 2 2 cbsn+2 – 4 3 3 1 – timp perc hp – str
Autograph MS   held by the BBC Music Library (MS 2902)
First transmission   (using Arnold's signature tune) 22 March 1959

1960

294   PARASOL   53'30"
A musical for television, commissioned by the BBC
Written by   Caryl Brahms and Ned Sherrin (book and lyrics), based on
   the 'Anatol' dialogues by Arthur Schnitzler
Producer   Ned Sherrin
Musical numbers staged by   Alfred Rodrigues
Musical numbers include:
   Overture
   Song: 'Only a parasol'
   Song: 'Face of love'
   Song: 'A woman would be lost without a man'
   Song: 'Goodbye champagne'
   Song: 'Sleep'
   Song: 'Who do I love?'
   Song: 'The other one?'
   Song: 'Don't think it hasn't been fun'
Autograph MS   full score untraced, piano reduction and some orchestral
   parts held by the BBC Music Library
Music played by   Eric Robinson Orchestra/Marcus Dods
Transmission date   20 March 1960 (pre-recorded 18 March 1960)
Publication   vocal album – B. Feldman & Co., 1961

1963

295   ESPIONAGE
Music for the ATV television series
Executive producer   Herbert Hirschman
First episode transmitted   5 October 1963

Arnold contributed music to 14 episodes of which manuscripts still exist
for the following:

'The Weakling'   20'07"
Instrumentation   1 0 bcl+1 0 – 1 1 1 0 – gtr perc pno – str (no dbs)

'A Covenant with Death' 13'10"
Instrumentation 1 0 bcl+1 0 – 1 1 1 0 – gtr perc cel – str (no dbs)
Recorded 29 August 1964

'He Rises on Sunday and We on Monday' 16'53"
Instrumentation 1 1 0 0 – 2 1 0 0 perc hp pno cel – str

'The Gentle Spy' 5'00"
Instrumentation 1 1 0 0 – 2 1 0 0 – perc pno hp – str

'The Dragon Slayer' 9'58"
Instrumentation 1 0 1 0 – 2 1 0 0 – gtr perc cel or pno – str

'To the Very End' 15'36"
Instrumentation picc+1 0 1 0 – 2 1 0 0 – gtr perc pno – str

'A Camel to Ride, a Sheep to Eat' 16'18"
Instrumentation 1 1 1 0 – 2 1 0 0 – gtr perc pno – str (no vns)
Recorded 24 October 1963

'The Light of a Friendly Star' 15'11"
Instrumentation 1 1 1 0 – 2 1 0 0 – gtr perc pno – str (no vns)
Recorded 24 October 1963

'A Tiny Drop of Poison' 17'13"
Instrumentation 1 0 1+asax 0 – 2 1 0 0 – gtr perc pno – str (no vns)

'Festival of Pawns' 18'43"
Instrumentation 1 2 0 0 – 2 1 2 1 – gtr perc pno – str (no vns)

'Never Turn your Back on a Friend' 13'29"
Instrumentation 0 0 1 0 – 0 1 2 0 – timp perc pno – str

'Medal for a Turned Coat' 9'48"
Instrumentation 0 0 1 0 – 0 1 2 0 – timp perc pno – str

'Sentence of Death'   19'48"
Instrumentation   1 0 bcl+1 0 – 2 1 0 0 – gtr perc pno – str (no vns)

'Do You Remember Leo Winters?'   5'12"
Instrumentation   1 0 bcl+1 0 – 2 1 0 0 – gtr perc pno – str (no vns)

'Espionage – Main Title, Bumper and End Title'   1'41"
Instrumentation   1 0 bcl+1 0 – 1 1 1 0 – gtr timp perc pno – str (no dbs)
Autograph MS   held by the Royal College of Music, London

296   GALA PERFORMANCE   1'30"
Signature tune for BBC TV series
I   Main Title: Allegro vivace
II   End Title: Allegro vivace
Instrumentation   2 2 2 2 – 4 2 3 1 – gtr timp 2perc hp – str
Autograph MS   revised version, held by the Royal College of Music,
    London
Music played by   Orchestra/Malcolm Arnold
First transmission   19 November 1963 (pre-recorded 27 October 1963)

A revised version of the opening and closing titles was recorded on
2 October 1964 and transmitted on 23 October 1964.

1965

297   THEME FOR PLAYER'S   0'45"
Written for John Player Tobacco as a TV advertising theme – it was not
    used
Autograph MS   piano score, held by the Royal College of Music,
    London

297a   THEME POUR MON AMIS   1'0"
Version of 'Theme for Player's' for whistler and piano

The title is a pun on the name of John Amis, for whose use the *Thême*
was intended.

1967

THE TURTLE DRUM   Opus 92   50'00"

A children's play for television (originally entitled *Kaisoo the Fisherboy*)
Commissioned by the BBC
Producer   John Hosier
Director   Moyra Gambleton
Music
  1   The Turtle Drum
  2   Go Back Where you Belong
  3   Round of Welcome
  4   Divertissement of the Deep
  5   The Four Seasons
  6   Sayonara Song
Instrumentation   fl/picc tpt gtr(s) perc db
Autograph MS   held by the BBC Music Library (MS 11595)
Music played by   James Blades and the David Livingstone Primary
   School
First performance   BBC Television, 26 April 1967 (the first programme in
   the series *Making Music*)
Publication   Oxford University Press, 1968, Faber Music, 1986

1968

THE FIRST LADY   2'03"

Opening and closing titles for the BBC TV series
Series devised by   Alan Plater
Series producer   David E. Rose
Music
  I   Main Title: Allegro – Vivace – Meno mosso – Allegro
  II   End Title: Moderato – Allegro
Instrumentation   0 0 0 0 – 0 picc tpt+2 3 1 – 2perc cel 2hp and s a t b
   chorus
Autograph MS   full score and piano reduction held by the BBC Music
   Library (MS 8675)
First transmission   7 April 1968

At the end of the series Arnold's theme was used in an arrangement for brass band by Ronnie Hazelhurst.

1977

300 HARD TIMES duration unknown
Theme music for ITV adaptation of the novel by Charles Dickens
Instrumentation 3fl ca 2hn 3tpt 3trb timp perc
Music played by Ensemble/Marcus Dods
Autograph MS untraced
First transmission 25 October 1977 (Granada Television)

The theme music is an arrangement by Marcus Dods of part of the Cavatina from the *Little Suite* No. 2 for Brass Band, op. 93 (**126**).

ARRANGEMENTS OF MUSIC BY OTHER COMPOSERS

1943

MOTET – MARIE ASSUMPTIO
Anon (13th century)
arr hn tpt trb
Autograph MS untraced
First performance Malcolm Arnold (tpt)/Dennis Brain(hn)/
George Maxted (trb); St Peter's Church, Eaton Square, London,
15 August 1943

DOUBLE-HOQUET
Guillaume de Machaut
arr tpt hn trb
Autograph MS untraced
First performance Malcolm Arnold (tpt)/Dennis Brain(hn)/
George Maxted (trb); St Peter's Church, Eaton Square, London,
15 August 1943

1948

ONLY A LITTLE BOX OF SOLDIERS
music-hall song arr voice and piano
Words Fred Leigh
Autograph MS untraced

1953

TANGO IN D
Isaac Albéniz: España, op. 165 no. 2
arr orchestra

Andantino grazioso
Instrumentation 2 2 2 2 – 4 2 3 0 – timp perc hp – str
Autograph MS untraced

1959

305 ON THE BROW OF RICHMOND HILL
Henry Purcell
song arr alto and string orchestra
Words Tom Durfey
Autograph MS untraced
First performance Pamela Bowden (a)/Richmond Community Centre
String Orchestra/Malcolm Arnold – Richmond Community Centre
Hall, Surrey, 26 March 1959

Written for Pamela Bowden

1960

306 CHRISTMAS CAROLS
Written for the Save The Children Fund
(i)   'The First Nowell' (Allegretto) arr gtr bar chorus and orchestra
       Instrumentation 2 2 2 2 – 4 2 3 1 – timp 2perc cel hp – str
(ii) 'Away in a Manger' (Moderato) arr orchestra
       Instrumentation 2 1 2 1 – 4 0 0 0 – glsp cel hp – str
(iii) 'Good King Wenceslas' (Allegro moderato) arr brass band and
       orchestra
       Instrumentation 2 1 2 1 – 4 2 2 1 perc pno hp – str
Autograph MS held by the Royal College of Music, London
First performance St Martin-in-the-Fields, London, 19 December 1960

1962

307 WE THREE KINGS OF ORIENT ARE
March arr piano and orchestra
Publication Henrees Music, 1962

1967

THOMAS MERRITT: CORONATION MARCH
arr brass band
Marziale – Trio – Marziale
Score completed　St Merryn, Cornwall, 17 December 1967
Autograph MS　held by the Royal College of Music, London
First performance　St Dennis Silver Band/St Agnes Silver Band/
　Malcolm Arnold, Truro Cathedral, Cornwall, 16 March 1968
Publication　Henrees Music, 1968

Merritt's march was composed in 1901 to celebrate the Coronation of
Edward VII. Arnold's score bears the preface:

> Thomas Merritt, the son of a copper miner, was born in Ilogan,
> Cornwall, on 26th October, 1863. He left school at the age of eleven
> to work in the mines. By natural talent and immense hard work he
> eventually became a Music Teacher and Organist. He composed a
> great deal of music and his carols are sung all over Cornwall and in all
> countries where Cornish people have emigrated. He died at the age of
> 46 on April 17th, 1908, and is buried at Ilogan Parish Churchyard,
> Cornwall.

1968

THOMAS MERRITT: ANTHEMS AND CAROLS
(i)　Carol: 'Awake with joy, Salute the morn'
　　arr s a t b chorus, two brass bands and orchestra
　　Allegro
　　Instrumentation　picc+2 2 2 2 – 4 3 3 1 – timp 3perc hp – str
　　Score completed　St Merryn, Cornwall, 12 January 1968
　　Autograph MS　held by the Royal College of Music, London
(ii)　Carol: 'Send out the light'
　　arr s a t b chorus and brass band
　　Allegro maestoso – Andante – Allegro con brio – Largamente
　　Score completed　St Merryn, Cornwall, 14 January 1968
　　Autograph MS　held by the Royal College of Music, London

(iii)   Anthem: 'The Eyes of all Wait for Thee'
        arr s a t b chorus, harp and strings
        Moderato – Andante pastorale – Allegro
        Score completed   St Merryn, Cornwall, 17 January 1968
        Autograph MS   held by the Royal College of Music, London
(iv)   Anthem: 'Awake up my Glory'
        arr s a t b chorus and orchestra
        Allegro moderato – Allegro maestoso – Allergro con spirito
        Instrumentation   picc+2 2 2 2 – 4 3 3 1 – timp 3perc – str
        Score completed   St Merryn, Cornwall, 17 January 1968
        Autograph MS   held by the Royal College of Music, London
First performance   Mixed Choirs/Penzance Orchestral Society/
    Cornwall Symphony Orchestra/St Agnes Silver Band/
    St Dennis Silver Band/Malcolm Arnold; Truro Cathedral, Cornwall,
    16 March 1968 (broadcast by the BBC on 17 April 1968)

1971

310   WILLIAM WALTON: SONATA FOR STRING
      ORCHESTRA
      arr of String Quartet (fourth movement only arr Arnold)
      I   Allegro
      II   Presto
      III   Lento
      IV   Allegro molto
      Instrumentation   strings (6 4 4 4 3)
      Autograph MS   held by Oxford University Press
      First performance   Academy of St Martin-in-the-Fields/Neville Marriner,
          Perth Festival, Australia, 2 March 1972
      Publication   Oxford University Press, 1973

In a letter to Stewart Craggs dated 3 December 1975 Malcolm Arnold
tells him:

> Knowing how he [Walton] hates, as don't we all, the physical labour
> of writing music, I offered to arrange the string quartet under his
> supervision, to which he readily agreed. I was completing a work of

my own and went out to Ischia to stay and do my work some three weeks later. When I arrived he had already completed the first two movements and was half-way through the slow movement. This did not surprise me, and the reason for my offer was to give him encouragement to do it himself. However, I stayed with him until I had completed the last movement under his supervision, and we more or less had a race, meeting for luncheon and dinner and reporting progress. I am sorry to say that he beat me by about two days, but after all mine was a quick movement with so many semi-quavers.

ADDENDUM

Since going to press, details of two new Arnold works have been announced:

1986

FOUR IRISH DANCES Opus 126   10'00"
for orchestra
2+picc 2 2 2 – 4 3 3 1 – timp 2 perc – str
I   Allegro con energico
II   Comodo
III   Piacevole
IV   Vivace
Score completed   18 June 1986
Autograph MS   held by the composer
Dedication   Donald Mitchell
Publication   Faber Music, 1986

FANTASY FOR DESCANT RECORDER Opus 127   11'00"
Vivace – Lento – Allegretto – Presto – A tempo
Score completed   9 June 1986
Dedication   Michala Petri
Publication   Faber Music, 1986

BIBLIOGRAPHY

ARTICLES AND LECTURES BY ARNOLD

'On the birth of a Dandipratt', *Winter Gardens Society Magazine*, Winter 1950
'The Serious Composer's approach to Film Music' – an illustrated lecture,
  Recital Room, Royal Festival Hall, 11 March 1954
'I Think of Music in Terms of Sound', *Music and Musicians*, July 1956, p. 9
'Finding the Money', *The Sunday Times*, 2 November 1958
'Prof. Hans Knappertsbusch', letter to *The Times*, 4 November 1965
'Don't shoot the pianist', *Guardian*, 3 June 1971
'Music' (Malcolm Arnold writes about the music he enjoys), *The Listener*,
  14 October 1971

GENERAL ARTICLES ON ARNOLD IN PERIODICALS AND NEWSPAPERS

'Malcolm Arnold, creater of Beckus', *Winter Gardens Society Magazine*, Winter
  1950
Alan Gregory: 'Malcolm Arnold, an Interview', *Philharmonic Post*,
  November/December 1951, pp. 8–10
Arthur Jacobs: 'Three Young Composers', *Picture Post*, 29 December 1951
'All made in Northampton', *Northampton Independent*, 1 May 1953
Andrew Porter: 'Music of Today: Malcolm Arnold', *London Musical Events*,
  December 1953, pp. 17–18
Scott Goddard: 'A Young British Symphonist', *The Listener*, li, 4 February 1954
Donald Mitchell: 'Malcolm Arnold', *Musical Times*, August 1955, pp. 410–13
Arthur Jacobs: 'Mr Arnold makes music say more than words', *Sunday Dispatch*,
  4 April 1958
'Malcolm Arnold – Anti-Theorist', *The Times*, 11 May 1959
Desmond Shawe-Taylor: 'Symphonic High Spirits', *The Sunday Times,*
  6 November 1960
Arthur Jacobs: 'Here is a new name to watch', *Reynolds News*, 13 November 1960

'Language of Modern Music in complete chaos' (Malcolm Arnold talks to the *Gloucestershire Echo*), 24 March 1961

'Artist and Composer', *Music Magazine*, May 1964

Arthur Hutchings: 'Malcolm Arnold: Music Without Words', *Faber Music News*, Summer 1968, pp. 11–13

'Sincerity in simplicity' (Malcolm Arnold talks to Christopher Ford), *Guardian Weekly*, 24 April 1971

Gillian Widdicombe: 'Arnold at 50', *Financial Times*, 18 October 1971

'Malcolm Arnold', *Strad*, February 1972

Edward Gregson: 'The Melody Maker', *Sounding Brass*, July 1973

Hugo Cole: 'Malcolm Arnold at 60', *Music and Musicians*, October 1981, pp. 9–11

BROADCAST TALKS AND INTERVIEWS BY AND ON ARNOLD

Note *BBC(SA)* indicates BBC Sound Archive and *NSA* National Sound Archive.

Interviewed by Bernard Palmer in series *The Composer Speaks*, *BBC(SA)* 25933 (13/5/59)

In Reminiscences of Sir Thomas Beecham in series *Music Magazine*, *BBC(SA)* 26894 (12/3/61)

Interviewed and used in series 'Talking About Music No. 23', *BBC(SA)* 27565 (8/9/61)

Interviewed by Ken Emrys Roberts on writing music for films, *BBC(SA)* 28653 (28/1/64)

Reference by Richard Rodney Bennett in interview on writing music for films, *BBC(SA)* 28652 (31/1/64)

Interviewed by Christopher Nupen for programme *Young Musicians in Britain Today*, *BBC(SA)* 29411/3 (4/64)

Talking about his music and method of working in series *Composer's Portrait*, *BBC(SA)* 30335 (9/12/65); *NSA* Tape M674W (28/12/65)

In *Constant Lambert; a Portrait*, *BBC(SA)* Tape T.30368 (11/6/66)

In *Sir Thomas Beecham: The Man and His Music*, a personal tribute introduced by John Amis, *BBC Artium* REGL 350 (broadcast 17/1/67, issued 1979, *UK4*)

Talking about his William Blake Songs, *BBC(SA)* 30984 (11/3/67)

Interviewed on his life and work, *BBC(SA)* 32102 (11/68); *NSA* Tape M2016W (9/10/70)

In *Reminiscences of Gerard Hoffnung*, *BBC(SA)* Tape T.32653 (22/9/69)

Talking about his Fourth Symphony, *NSA* Tape M 4243R (15/10/71)

A fiftieth birthday greeting by Humphrey Searle in series *Music Magazine*, *NSA* Tape M4242R (17/10/71)

Malcolm Arnold and the Curse of Popularity, talk by Donald Mitchell, *BBC(SA)* (14/3/77)

Interviewed by Michael Oliver in series *Music Weekly*, *NSA* Tape M8288BW (23/1/80)

Sixtieth birthday tribute by Arthur Peacock on Arnold's place in the twentieth-century symphonic tradition (21/10/81)

Interviewed by Sheridan Morley in series *Sheridan Morley meets* (first network broadcast, BBC 2, 6/12/84)

Interviewed by John Amis as birthday guest on *Midweek* programme (Radio 4, 23/10/85)

DISCOGRAPHY

In order for the Discography to be as comprehensive as possible, NSA Tapes, BBC Sound Archive and BBC Transcription Service discs have been included with standard commercial discs (a few important private acetates have also been included where they have historical interest). Commercial discs have been allocated an identifying number as follows:

1   78 rpm, 10″
2   78 rpm, 12″
3   33⅓ rpm, 10″
4   33⅓ rpm, 12″
5   45 rpm, 7″

The countries of origin are identified as UK, USA, USSR, E/C(Europe/ Commonwealth)

Additional abbreviations:
C	Cassette
CD	Compact Disc
D	Digital
EP	Extended Play
NSA	National Sound Archive
P	Privately recorded acetate
(R)	Re-issue
(SA)	Sound Archive (BBC)
(SQ)	Stereo/Quadrophonic
T	Tape
(TD)	Transcription Disc (BBC)
st	Stereo

Main sources consulted for the Discography include:
Gramophone (1948–85) and *Gramophone Classical Catalogue* (1953–85), General Gramophone Publications Ltd, Harrow, Middlesex
The Record Guide (1951), *The Record Year* (1952), *The Record Year 2* (1953), *The Record Guide* (1955), *The Record Guide Supplement* (1956), Edward Sackville-West and Desmond Shawe-Taylor, Collins, London

The World's Encyclopedia of Recorded Music (and Supplements) (1952, 1953 and 1957), F. F. Clough and G. J. Cuming, Sidgwick and Jackson Ltd, London

Schwann (1953–85), Schwann Record and Tape Catalogues, Boston, Massachusetts, USA

Guide to Modern Music on Records (1958), Robert Simpson and Oliver Prenn (eds.), Anthony Blond, London

Music on Record: A Critical Guide, vols. 1–4 (1962, 1963), Peter Gammond and Burnett James, Hutchinson and Co., London

The Stereo Record Guide, vols. 1–9 (1960–74), *The Penguin Stereo Record Guide* (1977), *The Guide to the Bargain Classics* (1962, 1964, 1965), *The New Penguin Guide to Bargain Records* (1980), *The New Penguin Stereo Record and Cassette Guide* (1982), *The Penguin Cassette Guide* (1979), Ivan March (ed.), Long Playing Record Library Ltd, Blackpool

Index to Record Reviews, vols. 1–5 (1978–80), Kurtz Myers (ed.), G. K. Hall and Co., Boston, Massachusetts, USA

Index to Tape and Record Reviews (1972–82), Antoinette O. Maleady, Chulainn Press, California, USA

Melodiya: A Soviet Russian LP Discography (1981), John R. Bennett, Greenwood Press, Connecticut, USA

The Technique of Film Music (1972), Roger Manvell and John Huntley (eds.), Focal Press, Sevenoaks, Kent

Film Music (1974) and *Keeping Score: Film Music 1972–79* (1981), James L. Limbacher (ed.), Scarecrow Press, New Jersey, USA

Music on Record 1: Brass Bands (1980), Peter Gammond and Raymond Horricks (ed.), Patrick Stephens Ltd, Cambridge

The Record Year 1 (1979) and *The Record Year 2* (1981), Bryan Crimp, Duckworth and Co. Ltd, London

WORKS BY ARNOLD

Africa – Texas Style (**278**)
Film available on Guild Home Video cassette

The Battle of Britain (**281**)
Film available on Warner Home Video cassette
Soundtrack: Orchestra/Malcolm Arnold, *United Artists* UAS 5201 (1/70, *USA4*); *United Artists* UAS 29019, st (9/69, *UK4*); (R) *Sunset* SLS 50407, st (10/77, *UK4*); (R) *Sunset* TC–50407 (*C*)
Other excs: Ron Goodwin and his Orchestra, *Studio Two* TWOX 1007, st (*UK4*); *EMI* (NZ) SLZ 8346, st/SLZ 8582, st (*E/C4*); *EMI* (NZ) EMSS–2 (*E/C4*)

Anniversary Overture, op. 99 **(133)**
BBC Northern Symphony Orchestra/Malcolm Arnold, *NSA* Tape M 1887W
Lisbon Conservatoire Orchestra/Peter Michaels, *Aries* LP 1622, st (*USA4*, pirate
    recording of above)
Light Music Society/Malcolm Arnold, *BBC(TD)* 128116

Beckus the Dandipratt, op. 5 **(17)**
London Philharmonic Orchestra/Eduard van Beinum, *London* T.5231 *(USA2)*;
    Decca K.1844 (7/48, *UK2*)
Royal Philharmonic Orchestra/Malcolm Arnold, *Philips* NBL 5021 (12/55,
    UK4); *Philips* NBE 11038 (9/56, *UK5*); *Epic* LC 3422 (5/58, *USA4*); *Philips Int.*
    N.10712L *(E/C4)*
Bournemouth Symphony Orchestra/Constantin Silvestri, *BBC (TD)* X418902
Royal Liverpool Philharmonic Orchestra/Sir Charles Groves, *BBC(TD)*
    142880–SQ (1978)
London Symphony Orchestra/Nicholas Braithwaite, *Lyrita* SRCS 95, st (1/80,
    UK4)
Bournemouth Symphony Orchestra/Malcolm Arnold, *HMV* ASD 3823,
    st (6/80, *UK4*); *HMV* TC – ASD 3823 (C); *EMI Int.* 063–07174, st *(E/C4)*;
    (R) *HMV Greensleeve* ESD 1077801, st (9/83, *UK4*); (R) *HMV Greensleeve*
    TC–ESD 1077804 (C)

The Bridge on the River Kwai **(254)**
Soundtrack: Overture, The River Kwai March*; Shear's Escape, Nicholson's
    Victory, Sunset, Working on the Bridge, Trek to the Bridge, Camp Concert
    Dance, Finale: Royal Philharmonic Orchestra/Malcolm Arnold and Mitch
    Miller and his Orchestra*, *Columbia* CL 1100 (2/58, *USA4*); (R) *Columbia*
    CS 9426, st (9/70, *USA4*)
Soundtrack excs: Nicholson's Victory, Working on the Bridge, Camp Concert
    Dance, Finale: Royal Philharmonic Orchestra/Malcolm Arnold, *Philips* BBE
    12194 (7/58, *UK5*)
Soundtrack exc: The River Kwai March: Mitch Miller and his Orchestra, *Philips*
    PB 777 (1/58, *UK1*); (R) *Philips* BBR 8117 *(UK3)*; (R) *Philips* BBR 8121
    (UK3), (R) *Reader's Digest* (set) RDS 10026, st (8/84, *UK4*); *Reader's Digest* (set)
    RDC 91114 (C)
Other excs: The River Kwai March (orchestral arrs): Ron Goodwin and his
    Concert Orchestra, *Parlophone* R 4391 (1/58, *UK1*); *Parlophone* GEP 8722
    (UK5).
Ray Martin and his Orchestra, *Columbia* SX 1093/SCX 3255, st (7/58, *UK4*)
Eddie Barclay and his Orchestra, *Felsted* PDL 85054/ESD 3066, st (11/58, *UK4*)
Orchestra/Morris Stoloff, *Pye* NPL 28002 (7/59), *UK4*); (R) *Marble Arch* MAL
    1292 *(UK4)*
Frank Chacksfield and his Orchestra, *Decca* ACL 1073 (9/61, *UK4*)
Cleveland 'Pops' Orchestra/Louis Lane, *Epic* LC 3809/BC 1147, st (12/61,

USA4); *Columbia* SX 6048/SCX 6048, st (6/66, *UK4*)

Ancleng Orchestra, *BBC(SA)* 29410 (rec. 11/64)

London Festival Orchestra/Stanley Black, *Decca Phase Four* PFS 4350, st (*UK4*); *Decca Phase Four* KPFC 4350 (*C*)

Geoff Love and his Orchestra, *Music for Pleasure* MFP 5171/SMFP 5171, st (4/71, *UK4*)

London Concert Orchestra/Bob Leaper, *Sunset* SLS 50339, st (4/73, *UK4*)

Hans Bertram and his Orchestra, *Polydor* 2371 238, st (11/75, *UK4*)

Bev Phillips and his Orchestra, *Warwick* WW 5012, st (4/76, *UK4*)

London Philharmonic Orchestra/Geoff Love, *Music for Pleasure* GLM 0001 (*UK4*); (R) *Music for Pleasure* MFP 50452 (*UK4*)

The River Kwai March (arr military band): West German Army Band, *Urania* UX 133/USD 1033, st (12/59, *E/C4*)

Band of the Grenadier Guards/Lt. Col. Rodney Bashford, *London* PS 434, st (*USA4*); *Decca* LK 4669 (6/65, *UK4*); (R) *Decca Phase Four* PFS 4066, st (6/65, *UK4*); (R) *Decca* PA 18/SPA 18, st (*UK4*); (R) *Decca* KCSP 18 (*C*) (and cartridge ECSP 18); (R) *Decca* FOS 17, st (*UK4*)

Royal Dragoons Band/D. H. Mackay, *Royal Dragoons* LP 70003 (7/72, *UK4*)

Glasgow Highlanders Regimental Band/T. J. Hanlon, *Thistle* BSLP 46 (*UK4*)

Massed Bands/Lt. Col. T. Sharpe (arr Osterling), *Pye* PKD 2001/1, st (9/75, *UK4*)

Die Grosse Garde Regimentsmusik/Robert Stolz, *BASF* 292 2116,st (10/75, *E/C4*)

The River Kwai March (other arrs): Hohner Accordion Orchestra/Heinz Funk, *Saga* XID 5144 (*UK4*)

Zacharias and his Magic Violins (with whistling!), *Polydor* LPHM 46081 (*UK4*); *Polydor* LPHM 46428 (*UK4*)

Amiable and his accordion and organ with vocal and instrumental ensemble, *Vogue* TDF 1 *(UK4)*

Pierre Dorsey (pno) and his Orchestra, *Vogue* VRL 3012 (*UK4*)

Other excs (not identified): *Capitol* T.1986/ST.1986, st (*USA4*); *Colpix* (S) CP.458, st, and CP.464, st (*USA4*); *Dunhill* (S) 50015, st (*USA4*); *Kapp* KL 1005/KL(S) 3005, st (*USA4*); *London* LL 3106/PS 159, st (*USA4*); *MGM* SC 3894 st/SE 3988 st/SE 4132 st (*USA4*); *RCA* LM 2381/LSC 2381, st (10/60, *USA4*);*Warner Bros* B.1247/WS 1319, st (*USA4*); *Wing* 12504 (*USA4*)

Candlemas Night (**288**)
Ad hoc ensemble (8 players), *BBC(SA)* 22791 (18/11/55)

The Captain's Paradise (**223**)
Exc only: *MGM* SE 4271, st (*USA4*)

The Chalk Garden (**273**)
Exc: Madrigal: Andy Williams (vocal)/Orchestra/Robert Mersey, *CBS* BPG

62372 (4/64, *UK4*); *CBS* AAG 192 (*UK5*)
Kellie Greene (pno) with orchestra, *Stateside* SS 303 (6/64, *UK5*)
Carmen Cavallaro (pno) with rhythm accompaniment, *Brunswick* LAT 8624
   (*UK4*); *MCA* MUP 359/MUPS 359, st (1/66, *UK4*)
The Wayfarers (instrumental), *Decca* F.12339 (2/66, *UK5*)

Commonwealth Christmas Overture, op. 64 (**86**)
London Symphony Orchestra/Alexander Gibson, *BBC(TD)* 128775

Concerto for 2 Pianos (3 Hands) and Orchestra, op. 104 (**139**)
Phyllis Sellick/Cyril Smith/BBC Symphony Orchestra/Malcolm Arnold,
   BBC(SA) Tape T.33131 (16/8/69); *BBC(TD)* 126299; *NSA* Tape M.1659W
Phyllis Sellick/Cyril Smith/City of Birmingham Symphony Orchestra/Malcolm
   Arnold, *HMV* ASD 2612, st (10/70, *UK4*); *EMI Int.* 063-04545, st (*E/C4*);
   (R) *HMV Greensleeve* ESD 7065, st (11/78, *UK4*); (R) *HMV Greensleeves*
   TC–ESD 7065 (2/79, *C*)

Concerto for 28 Players, op. 105 (**140**)
Northern Sinfonia/Steuart Bedford, *NSA* Tape 3516 BW (20/6/79)

Concerto for Clarinet and Strings, op. 20 (**34**)
Janet Hilton/BBC Northern Symphony Orchestra/Malcolm Arnold, *NSA* Tape
   M 1967 R
Janet Hilton/Bournemouth Sinfonietta/Norman del Mar, *EMI* EL 27 0264 1,
   st/D (8/85, *UK4*); *EMI* EL 27 0264 4 (*C*)

Concerto for Flute and Strings, op. 45 (**64**)
Gareth Morris/BBC Northern Orchestra/Malcolm Arnold, *BBC(SA)* Tape
   T.28485 (21/3/63); *NSA* Tape 0 58 R
John Solum/Philharmonia Orchestra/Neville Dilkes, *HMV(SQ)* ASD 3487,
   st (9/78, *UK4*); *HMV* TC-ASD 3487 (*C*); *EMI Int.* 063-06631Q (*E/C4*)
Richard Adeney/Bournemouth Sinfonietta/Ronald Thomas, *HMV* ASD 3868,
   st (7/80, *UK4*); *HMV* TC-ASD 3868 (*C*); *EMI Int.* 063-07290, st (*E/C4*)

Concerto for Guitar and Chamber Orchestra, op. 67 (**93**)
Julian Bream/Melos Ensemble/Malcolm Arnold, *RCA* LM 2487/LSC 2487, st
   (3/61, *USA4*); *RCA* RB 16252 (8/61, *UK4*); *RCA* SB 6826, st (4/70, *UK4*);
   RCA R85 – 1007/R85 – 5016 (*C*); (R) *RCA* (set) CRL3 0997, st (*USA4*);
   (R) *RCA* (set) ARL 3 0997, st (2/76, *UK4*); (R) *RCA Gold Seal* AGLI – 3883
   (9/81, *USA4*); (R) *RCA Gold Seal* GL 13883, st (11/81, *UK4*); (R) *RCA
   Gold Seal* GK 13883 (11/81, *C*)
John Williams/London Sinfonietta/Elgar Howarth, *CBS* 76715, st (9/78, *UK4*
   and *E/C4*); *CBS* 40-76715 (*C*); *Columbia* M-36680, st (*USA4*); *Columbia*
   MT-36680 (*C*)

Concerto for Harmonica and Orchestra, op. 46 (**65**)
Tommy Reilly (orchestra and conductor not identified), Acetate (no date, *P*)
Tommy Reilly/BBC Concert Orchestra/Vilem Tausky, *NSA* Tape 023R2
  (28/4/64)
Tommy Reilly/BBC Concert Orchestra/Henry Krips, *BBC(TD)* 115213
Larry Adler/Royal Philharmonic Orchestra/Morton Gould, *RCA* SB 6786,
  st (1/69, *UK4*); *Victor* LSC 3078, st (8/69, *USA4*); (R) *RCA Gold Seal*
  GL 42747, st (3/79, *UK4*); (R) *RCA Gold Seal* GK 42747 (*C*)
Tommy Reilly/London Sinfonietta/David Atherton, *Argo* ZRG 905, st (1/80,
  UK4)

Concerto for Oboe and Strings, op. 39 (**55**)
Leon Goossens/Boyd Neel Orchestra/Boyd Neel, Acetate (10/1/54, *P*)
Janet Craxton/BBC Scottish Orchestra/George Malcolm, *NSA* Tape M 998R
  (16/11/66)
Gordon Hunt/Bournemouth Sinfonietta/Norman del Mar, *EMI* EL 27 0264 1,
  st/D (8/85, *UK4*); *EMI* EL 27 0264 4 (*C*)

Concerto for Organ and Orchestra, op. 47 (**66**)
Hugh McClean/London Philharmonic Orchestra/Sir Adrian Boult, *BBC(SA)*
  22653/6 (21/11/55)
Hugh McClean/CBC Vancouver Orchestra/John Avison, *CBC* SM 129,
  st (*E/C4*)

Concerto for Piano Duet and Strings, op. 32 (**48**)
Susan Bradshaw/Richard Rodney Bennett/BBC Scottish Symphony
  Orchestra/Graham Treacher, *NSA* Tape 1094W (2/11/67)

Concerto for Trumpet and Orchestra, op. 125 (**165**)
John Wallace/Bournemouth Sinfonietta/Norman del Mar, *EMI* EL 27 0264 1,
  st/D (8/85, *UK4*); *EMI* EL 27 0264 4 (*C*)

Concerto for Two Violins and Strings, op.77 (**108**)
Alfredo Campoli/Derek Collier/London Symphony Orchestra/Malcolm
  Arnold, *BBC(SA)* Tape MT. 32898 (26/9/65); *NSA* Tape M 524R (28/12/65)
Alan Loveday/Granville Jones/London Philharmonic Orchestra/Malcolm
  Arnold, *BBC(SA)* Tape T.30860 (5/8/66); *BBC(TD)* 122845
Paul Kling/Peter McHugh/Louisville Orchestra/Jorge Mester, *Louisville* LS –
  731, st (4/74, *USA4*); *RCA Gold Seal* GL 25018, st (10/76, *UK4*)

Concerto for Viola and Chamber Orchestra, op. 108 (**144**)
Roger Best/Northern Sinfonia/Malcolm Arnold, *BBC(SA)* Tape T.35550
  (18/10/71); *NSA* Tape M 4424W (3/5/72)

Concerto No. 2 for Clarinet and Orchestra, op. 115 (**153**)
Benny Goodman/Park Lane Music Players/Malcolm Arnold, *Classic Record
  Library* 30–5550 (*USA4*); *BBC(TD)* 1402 62
Jack Brymer/BBC Concert Orchestra/Ashley Lawrence, *NSA* M 7621 BW
  (31/8/78)

Concerto No. 2 for Flute and Orchestra, op. 111 (**148**)
Richard Adeney/English Chamber Orchestra/Malcolm Arnold, *BBC(TD)*
  1883.02
John Solum/Philharmonia Orchestra/Neville Dilkes, *HMV(SQ)* ASD 3487,
  st (9/78, *UK4*); *HMV* TC-ASD 3487 (*C*); *EMI Int.* 063-06631Q (*E/C4*)
Richard Adeney/Bournemouth Sinfonietta/Ronald Thomas, *HMV* ASD 3868,
  st (7/80, *UK4*); *HMV* TC–ASD 3868, st (*C*); *EMI Int.* 063–07290, st (*E/C4*)

Concerto No. 2 for Horn and Strings, op. 58 (**80**)
Alan Civil/English Chamber Orchestra/Malcolm Arnold, *BBC(TD)* 125068
Alan Civil/Bournemouth Sinfonietta/Norman del Mar, *EMI* EL 27 0264 1,
  st/D (8/85, *UK4*); *EMI* EL 27 0264 4 (*C*)

Concert Piece for Percussion (**89**)
James Blades/Joan Goossens, *NSA* Tape M 1072R (30/12/66)
James Blades/Joan Goossens, *Discourses* ABK 13, st (7/74, *UK4*)

David Copperfield (**282**)
Soundtrack: Orchestra/Malcolm Arnold, *GRT* 10008, st (*USA4*); (R) *Label 'X'*
  10–1601 (*USA4*)

Divertimento No. 2, op. 75 (**105**)
Leicestershire Schools Symphony Orchestra/Eric Pinkett, *Pye Golden Guinea*
  GGC 4103/GSGC 14103, st (3/68, *UK4*)

Divertimento for Wind Trio, op. 37 (**53**)
A. Korneyev/A. Zaionts/V. Tupikin, *Melodiya* SM 02641/2, st (*USSR4*)
Douglas Whittaker/Janet Craxton/Colin Bradbury, *BBC(TD)* 122861
New London Wind Ensemble, *NSA* Tape M 485R (7/9/65)
Czech Philharmonic Wind Ensemble, *Supraphon* SUA 10582/SUAST 50582,
  st (11/74, *UK4*); *Supraphon* DV 6091/SV 8196, st (*E/C4*)
Members of the Interlochen Arts Wind Quintet, *Mark* MES 28486, st (*USA4*)
1st movement only: Members of the Westwood Wind Quintet, *Crystal* S-101,
  st (*USA4*)
Judith Pearce/Gareth Hulse/Michael Collins (Nash Ensemble), *Hyperion* A66173
  (5/86, *UK4*)

Duo for Flute and Viola, op. 10 (**22**)
Judith Pearce/Roger Chase (Nash Ensemble), *Hyperion* A66173 (5/86, *UK4*)

Duo for Two Cellos, op. 85 (**117**)
Christopher van Kampen/Moray Welsh (Nash Ensemble), *Hyperion* A66171
(5/86, *UK4*)

English Dances (Sets 1 and 2), op. 27 and op. 33 (**42** and **49**)
London Philharmonic Orchestra/Sir Adrian Boult, *London* LD 9178 (6/55,
USA3); *Decca* LW 5166 (6/55, *UK3*); *London* LLP 1335 (5/56, *USA4*); *Decca*
D 71096 (5/56 – Set 1 only – *UK5*); (R) *Ace of Clubs* ACL 113 (*UK4*); (R) *Eclipse*
ECS 646 (9/72, *UK4*); (R) *Decca* FOS 61/2 (2) (*UK4*)
Philharmonia Orchestra/Robert Irving, *Bluebird* LBC 1078 (*USA4*); *HMV* CLP
1172 (6/58, *UK4*); *Capitol* G 7105 (11/58, *USA4*)
BBC Northern Symphony Orchestra/Malcolm Arnold, *NSA* Tape M 1005W
(3/10/67)
Bournemouth Symphony Orchestra/Sir Charles Groves, *HMV(SQ)* ASD 3353,
st (6/77, *UK4*); *HMV* TC–ASD 3353 (*C*); *EMI Int.* 063–06383Q, st (*E/C4*);
(R) *HMV Greensleeve* ESD 1077801, st (9/83, *UK4*); (R) *HMV Greensleeve*
TC–ESD 1077804 (*C*)
London Philharmonic Orchestra/Malcolm Arnold, *Lyrita* SRCS 109, st (3/79,*UK4*)
Set 1 only: BBC Northern Orchestra/Charles Groves, 'Recorded Sound
Productions' Acetate (5/9/51, *P*); *NSA* Tape T 5516W
Set 2 only: Glasgow Schools' First Orchestra/Bryden Thomson, Barrie Hall
HAL 2874 (1964, *UK4*)
Set 1, Nos. 1 and 2; Set 2, Nos. 5, 6 and 8: Bournemouth Symphony
Orchestra/Sir Charles Groves, (R) *HMV Greensleeve* ESD 1077351, st (6/83,
UK4); *HMV Greensleeve* TC–ESD 1077354 (*C*)
Set 1, No. 3; Set 2, No. 5 only: Philharmonia Orchestra/Malcolm Arnold,
Columbia SED 5529 (2/56, *UK5*)
Set 2, No. 1 only: Hallé Orchestra/Owain Arwel Hughes, *Classics for Pleasure*
CFP 414474–1, st (1/85, *UK4*); *Classics for Pleasure* CFP 414474–4 (*C*)

English Dances, op. 27, arr Johnstone (**42b**)
Cornell University Wind Ensemble, *Cornell* CUWE 27, st (1/81, *USA4*)

English Dances, op. 27, arr
Nos. 2 and 4 only: Royal Marines (Commando Forces) Band/Capt. W. W.
Shillito, *Decca* SB 703, st (4/74, *UK4*); (R) *Decca* FOS 61/2(2) (*UK4*)

Fanfare for a Royal Occasion (**77**)
Trumpeters of the Royal Military School of Music, Kneller Hall/Lt.-Col. G.
Evans, *NSA* Tape T2675 BW (20/11/79)

Fanfare for Louis (**141**)
Elgar Howarth and Stanley Woods (tpts), *Polydor* 2460 123, st (rec. 7/70, *UK4*)

Fantasy for Audience and Orchestra, op. 106 (**142**)
BBC Symphony Orchestra/Colin Davis, *BBC(SA)* Tape T.34140 (12/9/70);
  BBC(TD) 128085

Fantasy for Bassoon, op.86 (**118**)
Otto Eiffert, *Gasparo* GS 103, st (11/77, *USA4*)
Knut Sonstevold, *BIS* 122, st (2/80, *E/C4*)
Brian Wightman (Nash Ensemble), *Hyperion* A66172 (5/86, *UK4*)

Fantasy for Brass Band, op. 114[a] (**151**)
Cory Band/Major H. A. Kenney, *BBC(SA)* Tape T.36388; *NSA* Tape M5341
  BW (21/10/74)
Cory Band/Major H. A. Kenney, *Decca* SB 319, st (7/75, *UK4*)
GUS Band/Keith Wilkinson, *Merlin* MRF 85089, st/D (6/86, *UK4*);
  MRFC 85089 (*C*)
Scherzo only: Whitburn Burgh Band/Major Peter Parkes, *Polyphonic* PRL 018,
  st (1982, *UK4*), also on cassette

Fantasy for Clarinet, op.87 (**119**)
Lawrence Sobol, T.CRT–012 (live performance)
Michael Collins (Nash Ensemble), *Hyperion* A66172 (5/86, *UK4*)

Fantasy for Flute, op. 89 (**121**)
Judith Pearce (Nash Ensemble), *Hyperion* A66172 (5/86, *UK4*)

Fantasy for Guitar, op.107 (**143**)
Julian Bream, *NSA* Tape M 5515 BW (5/5/75)

Fantasy for Harp, op. 117 (**156**)
Osian Ellis, *NSA* Tape M 7469 BW (8/5/78)

Fantasy for Horn, op. 88 (**120**)
Alan Civil, *NSA* Tape M 1016 W (11/10/67)
Lowell Greer, *Coronet* 3100, st (9/82, *USA4*)
John Pigneguy (Nash Ensemble), *Hyperion* A66172 (5/86, *UK4*)

Fantasy for Oboe, op. 90 (**122**)
Gareth Hulse (Nash Ensemble), *Hyperion* A66172 (5/86, *UK4*)

Fantasy for Trombone, op. 101 (**136**)
John Iveson, *Argo* ZRG 851, st (7/77, *UK4* and *E/C4*)

Fantasy for Tuba, op. 102 (**137**)
John Fletcher, *Two Ten* TT001, st (3/78, *UK4*)

Five Pieces for Violin and Piano, op. 84 (**115**)
Derek Collier/Ernest Lush, *NSA* Tape M 725 W (29/1/66)
Stephen Levine/Peter Lawson, *Auracle* AUC 1002, st (4/82, *UK4*)
Marcia Crayford/Ian Brown (Nash Ensemble), *Hyperion* A66171 (5/86, *UK4*)

Five William Blake Songs, op. 66 (**91**)
Pamela Bowden (a)/BBC Northern Orchestra/Malcolm Arnold, *NSA* Tape
   M 722R (28/1/66).
Alfreda Hodgson (a)/BBC Northern Symphony Orchestra/Raymond Leppard,
   NSA Tape M 5729BW (19/3/76)

Four Cornish Dances, op. 91 (**123**)
City of Birmingham Symphony Orchestra/Malcolm Arnold, *HMV* ASD 2878,
   st (5/73, *UK4*); *HMV* TC–ASD 2878 (*C*); *EMI Int.* 063–05266, st (*E/C4*);
   (R) *HMV Greensleeve* ESD 1077801, st (9/83, *UK4*); (R) *HMV Greensleeve*
   TC–ESD 1077804 (*C*)
London Philharmonic Orchestra/Malcolm Arnold, *Lyrita* SRCS 109, st (3/79,
   UK4)
London Philharmonic Orchestra/Malcolm Arnold, *BBC(TD)* 64602

Four Scottish Dances, op. 59 (**81**)
Philharmonia Orchestra/Robert Irving, *Bluebird* LBC 1078 (*USA4*); *HMV* CLP
   1172 (6/58, *UK4*); *Capitol* G.7105 (11/58, *USA4*)
London Philharmonic Orchestra/Malcolm Arnold, *Everest* LPBR 6021/SDBR
   3021, st (7/59, *USA4*); (R) *World Record Club* T.99/ST.99, st (1/62, *UK4*);
   (R) *Everest* SDBR 3021, st (1/69, *UK4*); (R) *Desto* DC 6448, st (9/78, *USA4*)
Scottish National Orchestra/Alexander Gibson, *Waverley* LLP 1010/SLLP 1010,
   st (12/62, *UK4*); *Waverley* YLP 060/XYLP 061, st (4/65, *UK5*)
National Philharmonic Orchestra/Charles Gerhardt, *RCA* GL 25006, st (10/76,
   UK4); *RCA* GK 25006
London Philharmonic Orchestra/Malcolm Arnold, *Lyrita* SRCS 109, st (3/79,
   UK4)
No. 1 only: Philharmonia Orchestra/George Weldon, *HMV* CLP 1645 (6/63,
   UK4); *HMV* CSD 1495, st (6/63, *UK4*); *HMV Concert Classics* SXLP 30243,
   st (11/78, *UK4*); (R) *HMV Concert Classics* TC–SXLP 30243 (*C*)
National Philharmonic Orchestra/Charles Gerhardt, *Reader's Digest* RDS 6681
   (rec. 9/71, *UK4*)

Nos. 2 and 4 only: Lancashire Schools Symphony Orchestra/Malcolm Doley,
  Abbey LPB 777, st (*UK4*)

Four Scottish Dances, op. 59 (1957 arr) (**81a**)
Interlochen High School Symphonic Band/George C. Wilson, *Golden Crest*
  GC 403 (*USA4*)

Four Scottish Dances, op. 59 (1957 arr) (**81b**)
No. 2 only: Band of the Royal Scots Guards, *EMI Note* NTS 162,st (2/79, *UK4*);
  EMI Int. OC 058–06879, st (*E/C4*)

A Grand, Grand Overture, op. 57 (**79**)
Morley College Symphony Orchestra/Malcolm Arnold, *Angel* 35500 (*USA4*);
  (R) *Angel* S 37028 (*USA4*); *Columbia* 33CX 1406 (1/57, *UK4*); (R) *HMV* (set)
  SLS 870(3) (3/75, *UK4*); (R) *HMV* (set) SLS 5069(3) (11/76, *UK4*); (R) *EMI
  Int.* (set) 153-52125/7 (*E/C4*)
Royal Philharmonic Orchestra/Malcolm Arnold, *Columbia* SED 5542 (12/57,
  UK5)
Heriot's School Orchestra/Martin Rutherford, *Heriot's* TD 7222, st (1977, *UK4*)

The Heroes of Telemark (**275**)
Film available on Rank Video Library cassette 0068C
Soundtrack: Orchestra/Malcolm Arnold, *Mainstream* 56064/S.6064, st (5/66,
  USA4)

Hobson's Choice (**230**)
Film available on TEVP video cassette TXE 90 0203 4 and TVE 90 0203 2

Homage to the Queen, op. 42 (**59**)
Philharmonia Orchestra/Robert Irving, *HMV* CLP 1011 (2/54, *UK4*); *Victor*
  LM 2037 (7/57, *USA4*)

Homage to the Queen Ballet Suite, op. 42a (**60**)
London Symphony Orchestra/Alexander Gibson, *BBC(TD)* 128777

Homage to the Queen Ballet Suite, op. 42a (1953 arr) (**60a**)
Exc only: Royal Marines Band/Lt.-Col. Sir F. Vivian Dunn, *Columbia Studio 2*
  TWO 285, st (*UK4*); *Columbia Studio 2* TC–TWO 285 (*C*); (R) *EMI Note*
  NTS 123, st (6/77, *UK4*); (R) *EMI Note* TC–NTS 123 (*C*)

HRH The Duke of Cambridge, op. 60 (**82**)
Band of the Royal Military School of Music, Kneller Hall/Lt.-Col. Basil H.
  Brown, *HMV* CLP 1730 (*UK4*); *HMV* CSD 1538, st (*UK4*)

Band of the Grenadier Guards/Major R. B. Bashford, *NSA* Tape M1513W
(9/9/68)
Band of the Grenadier Guards/Major Peter Parkes, *Decca* SKL 5096, st (11/71,
UK4); (R) *Decca* (set) D141 D 4, st (9/79, *UK4*); (R) *Decca* (set) K141 K4 (*C*)
Band of the Irish Guards/Major M. G. Lane, *Bandleader* BND 1002, st (6/82
UK4) (and on cassette)
Massed Bands of the Queen's Division/Peter Hannan, *DR* DR 35 (rec. 4/81,
UK4)
Band of the Grenadier Guards/Major D. R. Kimberley, *Unicorn-Kanchana* DKM
6000, st (6/83, *UK4*); (R) *Unicorn-Kanchana* DMC 6000 (*C*)

I Am a Camera (**240**)
Film available on CBS/Fox video cassette

The Inn of the Sixth Happiness (**258**)
Soundtrack: Royal Philharmonic Orchestra/Malcolm Arnold, *Fox*
M.3011/S.3011, st (3/59, *USA4*)
Soundtrack excs: Royal Philharmonic Orchestra/Malcolm Arnold, *Vega* 45P 138
(*E/C5*)
Other excs: Title Song and Children's March: Children of Dr Barnardo's
Home/Bill Shepherd and his Orchestra, *Nixa* 7N 15180 (12/58, *UK1*); *Nixa*
45–15180 (*UK5*)
Children/Cyril Stapleton and his Orchestra with vocal refrain by Bill Elliott,
Decca F.11094 (12/58, *UK1*); *Decca* 45F.11094 (UK5)
Theme music: Victor Sylvester and his Ballroom Orchestra, *Columbia* DB 4240
(1/59, *UK1*); *Columbia* 45DB 4240 (*UK5*)
The Four Aces (vocal)/Orchestra/Jack Pleis, *Brunswick* 05773 (1/59, *UK1*);
Brunswick 45-05773 (*UK5*); *Brunswick* OE 9458 (EP) (*UK5*)
Knightsbridge Strings/Malcolm Lockyer, *Top Rank* RX 3017 (7/59, *UK4*)
Frank Chacksfield and his Orchestra, *Decca* ACL 1073 (9/61, *UK4*)
The Wayfarers (instrumental) with orchestra, *Decca* F.11473 (6/62, *UK5*)
Children's March: Band of the Grenadier Guards/Lt.-Col. Rodney Bashford,
London PS 434, st (*USA4*)
Royal Philharmonic Orchestra/Ron Goodwin (in medley 'Memories of Ingrid
Bergman'), *EMI* EMS 1077691, st (1/84, *UK4*); *EMI* TC–EMS 1077694 (*C*)
Other excs (not identified): *London* LL 3298/PS 298, st (*USA4*); *RCA* LM
2381/LSC 2381, st (10/60, *USA4*)

The Inspector (**269**)
Theme: Ferrante and Teicher (2 pnos)/Orchestra/Nick Perito, *HMV Pop* 1028
(6/62, *UK5*)
Emmanuel Vardi and his Orchestra, *Kapp* KL 1289 (*USA4*)
Lisa's Theme: The Wayfarers (instrumental) with orchestra, *Decca* F.11473 (6/62,
UK5)

The Paul Smith Quartet, *MGM* C.911 (12/62, *UK4*)
Don Costa and his Chorus and Orchestra, *CBS (Realm)* RM 52086 (*UK4*)

Island in the Sun (**252**)
Theme: Gary Hughes and his Orchestra, *Reader's Digest* (set) RDM 2315 (1968, *UK4*)

It Started in Paradise (**219**)
Exc: (song) 'Young Love': Diana Decker/Orchestra/Muir Mathieson, *Rank* F. M. (No.?) (*UK2*); *BBC (SA)* 18166 (9/12/52)

John Clare Cantata, op. 52 (**72**)
Donald and Geoffrey Greed/BBC Northern Singers/Stephen Williams, *NSA* Tape M 382 R (20/2/68)
Celia Arieli/Peter Wallfisch/BBC Chorus/Peter Gellhorn, *NSA* Tape M 2031 R (2/11/70)
Nos. 1–3 only: BBC Chorus/Alexander Gibson, P. Levy's disc (16/4/56)
Exc – Autumn: BBC Northern Singers/Stephen Wilkinson, *BBC(TD)* 131716 (16/7/72)

The Key (**256**)
Soundtrack: Orchestra/Malcolm Arnold, *Columbia* CL 1185 (8/58, *USA4*)
Excs: Theme – The Key to your Heart: Mitch Miller and his Chorus and Orchestra with Jimmy Carroll (sax), *Philips* PB 847 (8/58, *UK1*); *Philips* PB 45–847 (*UK5*)
Other excs (not identified): *Warner Bros* B.1247/WS 1319, st (*USA4*)

Leonora No. 4 (Beethoven–Strasser) (**107**)
Morley College Symphony Orchestra/Norman del Mar, *Columbia* 33 CX 1785/SAX 2433, st (2/62, *UK4*); (R) *Angel* S–37028 (1974, *USA4*); (R) *HMV* (set) SLS 870(3) (3/75, *UK4*); (R) *HMV* (set) SLS 5069 (3) (11/76, *UK4*); (R) *EMI Int.* (set) 153 – 52125/7 (*E/C4*)

The Lion (**270**)
Soundtrack: Orchestra/Malcolm Arnold, *London* M.76001 (2/63, *USA4*)
Soundtrack excs (Opening Music, Love Theme, Dance of Happiness, Death of King, End Title): Orchestra/Malcolm Arnold, *Decca* DFE 8507 (12/62, *UK5*)

Little Suite No. 1, op. 53 (**73**)
March only: Pro Arte Orchestra/Gilbert Vinter, *HMV* CLP 1836 (*UK4*); *HMV* CSD 1588, st (2/65, *UK4*); *Capitol* P. 8642/SP.8642, st (10/66, *USA4*); (R) *World Record Club* ST 978, st (9/69, *UK4*)

Little Suite No. 1, op. 53, arr Sumner (**73a**)
March only: Royal Marines Band/Lt.-Col. Sir F. Vivian Dunn, *HMV* CLP 1684
   (*UK4*); *HMV* CSD 1515, st (12/63, *UK4*); (R) *Starline* SRS 5112, st (*UK4*);
   (R) *Executive* TC-EXE 59 (*C*)
Band of the Scots Guards/Capt. J. H. Howe, *Fontana* TL 5360/STL 5360,
   st (12/66, *UK4*)
Regimental Band of the Coldstream Guards/Capt. R. A. Ridings, *Rediffusion*
   Gold Star 15–20, st (8/75, *UK4*); (R) *Peerless* DT 021A (*UK4*)
Royal Marines (Naval Home Command, Portsmouth) Band/Capt. J. R. Mason,
   State Prima PRIM 4, st (2/79, *UK4*)
Band of the Grenadier Guards/Major D. R. Kimberley, *Unicorn* UNS 269D,
   st (*UK4*); (R) *Unicorn-Kanchana* DKM 6000, st (6/83, *UK4*); (R)
   Unicorn-Kanchana DMC 6000 (*C*)

Little Suite No. 1 for Brass Band, op. 80 (**112**)
Hanwell Band/Eric Bravington, *NSA* Tape M. 635W (30/11/65)
Black Dyke Mills Band/Roy Newsome, *Pye* NPL 18209/NSPL 18209, st (1968,
   UK4); (R) *Pye Golden Hour* GH 632, st (7/77, *UK4*); (R) *Pye Golden Hour*
   ZCGH 632 (*C*)
Fairey Engineering Works Band/Kenneth Dennison, *Decca* SB 301, st (11/72,
   UK4); (R) *Decca* SPA 413, st (*UK4*); (R) *Decca* KCSP 413 (*C*)
National Youth Brass Band of Great Britain/Geoffrey Brand, *Pye* GGL 10428/
   GSGL 10428, st (2/68, *UK4*); (R) *World Record Club* T 391/ST 391, st (*UK4*)
Yorkshire Imperial Metals Band/Dennis Carr, *Silverline* DJSL 034, st (*UK4*)
Yorkshire Imperial Metals Band/Trevor Walmsley, *DJM* DJM 46034, st (*UK4*);
   DJM DJB 46034 (*C*)
Finale only: Royal Doulton Band/Ted Gray, *Chandos* ABRD 1030(D) (7/81,
   UK4); *Chandos* ABRT 1030 (*C*)

Little Suite No. 2, op. 78 (**109**)
Atlantic Symphony Orchestra/Kenneth Elloway, *CBC* SM 215, st (rec. 10/71,
   E/C4)

Little Suite No. 2 for Brass Band, op. 93 (**126**)
Brighouse & Rastrick/Carlton Main Frickley Colliery and Grimethorpe Colliery
   Institute Bands/Malcolm Arnold, *NSA* Tape M1230R (19/8/68)
Black Dyke Mills Band/Geoffrey Brand, *Paxton* LPT 1028/SLPT 1028, st (1/69,
   UK4)
National Youth Brass Band of Great Britain/Geoffrey Brand, *World Record Club*
   ST 891, st (*UK4*)
City of London Brass Band/Geoffrey Brand, *Decca* SB 313, st (9/74, *UK4*)
City of Oxford Youth Band/Terry Brotherhood, *Rediffusion Gold Star* 15–56,
   st (1/77, *UK4*)

Black Dyke Mills Band/Roy Newsome, *Polyphonic* FB 102, st (*UK4*)
Clacton-on-Sea Co-operative Band/R. Howard, *Polyphonic* PRL 018, st (1982,
   UK4) (also on cassette)
Galop only: Watney Silver Band/Albert Meek, *Saga Eros* 8129 (*UK4*)

Nine Hours to Rama (**271**)
Soundtrack: Orchestra/Malcolm Arnold, *London* 76002 (8/63, *USA4*); *Decca* LK
   4527/SKL 4527, st (5/63, *UK4*)

No Love for Johnnie (**266**)
Theme song: Gerry Beckles (vocal)/Orchestra/Johnny Douglas, *Oriole* 45CB
   1606 (2/61, *UK5*)

Oboe Quartet, op. 61 (**83**)
London Oboe Quartet, *BBC(TD)* 127477; *NSA* Tape M 1608W (25/6/69); *NSA*
   Tape M 1835R (27/7/70)
Eileen Dickinson (ob)/Reginald Stead (vn)/Joan Butler (va)/Nigel Blemiley (vc),
   NSA Tape M 4044W (16/7/71)
Gareth Hulse/Marcia Crayford/Roger Chase/Christopher van Kampen (Nash
   Ensemble), *Hyperion* A66173 (5/86, *UK4*)

The Padstow Lifeboat, op. 94 (**127**)
BMC Concert Band/Harry Mortimer, *NSA* Tape M 1153 W (11/12/67)
BMC Concert Band/Harry Mortimer, *HMV* CLP 3650/CSD 3650, st (5/68,
   UK4); (R) *Starline* SRS 5105, st (8/72, *UK4*); (R) *Studio 2* TWOX 1048, st
   (3/76, *UK4*); (R) *Studio 2* TC-TWOX 1048 (C) (and cartridge – same number);
   (R) *EMI Int.* OC 062-05989 (*UK4* and *E/C4*)
Black Dyke Mills Band/Geoffrey Brand, *Pye* NPL 18209/NSPL 18209, st (5/68,
   UK4); (R) *Pickwick* DTO 10052(2) (C)
Massed Bands/Malcolm Arnold, *NSA* Tape M 1261R (19/8/68)
Cory Band/Hoffman and Pollard (Newark) Works Band/Major H. A. Kenney,
   BBC(SA) Tape T.34499 (10/4/71)
Massed Bands/William Relton, *BBC* REH 207 (*UK4*); *BBC* RMC 4024 (C)
Royal Marines (Commando Forces) Band/Capt. W. W. Shillito, *Decca* SB 701, st
   (12/72, *UK4*); (R) *Decca* (set) D.141 D 4, st (9/79, *UK4*); (R) *Decca* (set) K 141
   D 4 (C); (R) *Decca* FOS 61/2(2), st (*UK4*)
City of London Brass Band/Geoffrey Brand, *Decca* SB 313, st (9/74, *UK4*)
Besses o' the Barn Band/Roy Newsome, *Crest Inc* – 81 – 12 (7/81, *USA4*)

Peterloo, op. 97 (**132**)
Royal Philharmonic Orchestra/Malcolm Arnold, *NSA* Tape M.1303R (7/6/68)
BBC Symphony Orchestra/Malcolm Arnold, *BBC(TD)* 124338
City of Birmingham Symphony Orchestra/Malcolm Arnold, *HMV* ASD 2878,

st (5/73, *UK4*); *HMV* TC-ASD 2878 (*C*); *EMI Int.* 063-05266, st (*E/C4*); (R) *HMV Greensleeve* ESD 1077801, st (9/83, *UK4*); (R) *HMV Greensleeve* TC-ESD 1077804 (*C*)

Philharmonic Concerto, op. 120 (**160**)
London Philharmonic Orchestra/Bernard Haitink, *BBC(TD)* 140401

Piano Trio, op. 54 (**74**)
Lyric Trio – Arthur Tabachnik (vn)/Shirley Evans (vc)/Hilda Freund (pno) – *Concert Disc* M.1234 (*USA4*); *Concert Disc* CS 234, st (7/63, *USA4*); (R) *Everest* SDBR 4234, st (4/72, *USA4*)
Marcia Crayford/Christopher van Kampen/Ian Brown (Nash Ensemble), *Hyperion* A66171 (5/86, *UK4*)

Quintet for Brass, op. 73 (**103**)
Hallé Brass Consort, *Pye Golden Guinea* GGC 4114/GSGC 14114, st (12/68, *UK4*)
Philip Jones Brass Ensemble, *Argo* ZRG 655, st (11/70, *UK4* and *E/C4*); *London Argo* ZRG 655, st (9/71, *USA4*); *BBC(TD)* 125069
City of London Brass Band, *Decca* SB 313, st (9/74, *UK4*)
Eastern Brass Ensemble, *Concord* S.1001, st (*USA4*); (R) *Klavier* 561, st (*USA4*)
Berlin Brass Quintet, *Crystal* S-201, st (1/75, *USA4*)
Ithaca Brass Quintet, *Mark* MES 32558, st (*USA4*)
Mount Royal Brass Quintet, *McGill University Records* 77004, st (3/79, *USA4*)
Canadian Brass Ensemble, *CBC* SM 239, st (*E/C4*); (R) *Moss Music Group* MMG 1123, st (3/81, *E/C4*); CMG 1123 (*C*); exc only: *Moss Music Group* MMG 1147, st (1/85, *E/C4*)
Budapest Brass Quintet, *Erato* STU 71410, st (10/81, *UK4* and *E/C4*); *Erato* MCE 71410 (*C*)
Equale Brass, *Nimbus* NIM 5004, CD (3/83, *UK*)
Fine Arts Brass Ensemble, *Happy Face* MMLP 1026, st (rec. 3/83, *UK4*)
Swedish Brass Quintet, *BIS* LP2, st (9/84, *E/C4*)

Quintet for Flute, Violin, Viola, Horn and Bassoon, op. 7 (**19**)
Wigmore Ensemble, *Troutbeck Acetate* (13/12/60, *P*); *NSA* Tape P2R1 (8/12/60)
Judith Pearce/Marcia Crayford/Roger Chase/John Pigneguy/Brian Wightman (Nash Ensemble), *Hyperion* A66173 (5/86, *UK4*)

Richmond (**87**)
Band of the Royal Military School of Music, Kneller Hall/Lt.-Col. Basil H. Brown, *HMV* CLP 1730 (*UK4*); *HMV* CSD 1538, st (*UK4*)
Trumpeters of the Royal Military School of Music, Kneller Hall, *BBC(SA)* 27408 (2/4/62); *NSA* Tape P6Q3 (19/11/63)

The Roots of Heaven (**257**)
Soundtrack: Orchestra/Malcolm Arnold, *Fox* M.3005/S.3005, st (3/59, *USA4*)

Salute to Thomas Merritt, op. 98 (**131**)
Penzance Orchestral Society/Cornwall Symphony Orchestra/St Dennis Silver
  Band/St Agnes Silver Band/Malcolm Arnold, *Hassell* HASLP 938/9 (*UK3*);
  NSA Tape 1168W (17/4/68)

'Sarabande' and 'Polka' from Solitaire (**76**)
Bournemouth Symphony Orchestra/Malcolm Arnold, *HMV* ASD 3823,
  st (6/80, *UK4*); *HMV* TC-ASD 3823 (*C*); *EMI Int.* 063–07174, st (*E/C4*);
  (R) *HMV Greensleeve* ESD 1077801, st (9/83, *UK4*); (R) *HMV Greensleeve*
  TC-ESD 1077804 (*C*)

Serenade for Guitar and Strings, op. 50 (**69**)
John Williams/BBC Concert Orchestra/John Carewe, *NSA* Tape 036R (18/7/64)
John Williams/English Chamber Orchestra/Sir Charles Groves, *CBS* 76634, st
  (12/77, *UK4* and *E/C4*); *CBS* 40-76634 (*C*); *Columbia* M-35172, st (*USA4*)

Serenade for Small Orchestra, op. 26 (**41**)
BBC Welsh Orchestra/Arwel Hughes, *NSA* Tape P 24 W2 (23/3/64)
Bournemouth Sinfonietta/Ronald Thomas, *HMV* ASD 3868, st (7/80, *UK4*);
  HMV TC-ASD 3868 (*C*); *EMI Int.* 063-07290, st (*E/C4*)
Park Lane Music Players/Malcolm Arnold, *BBC(TD)* 140259

Severn Bridge Variations on a Welsh Folk Song – composite work (**124**)
Theme and Variation 1: BBC Training Orchestra/Sir Adrian Boult, *NSA* Tape
  1099R (11/1/67)

Sinfonietta No. 1, op. 48 (**67**)
Northern Sinfonietta/Boris Brott, *Mace* MCS 9068, st (*USA4*)
Royal Liverpool Philharmonic Orchestra/Charles Groves, *NSA* Tape M 1104
  (24/11/67)
Philharmonia Orchestra/Neville Dilkes, *HMV(SQ)* ASD 3487, (9/78, *UK4*);
  HMV TC-ASD 3487 (*C*); *EMI Int.* 063-06631Q (*E/C4*)
English Chamber Orchestra/Malcolm Arnold, *BBC(TD)* 1883.02
London Symphony Orchestra/Nicholas Braithwaite, *Lyrita* SRCS 115, st (5/82,
  UK4)

Sinfonietta No. 2, op. 65 (**88**)
London Studio Orchestra/Malcolm Arnold, *NSA* Tape M 1108W (27/11/67)
Philharmonia Orchestra/Neville Dilkes, *HMV(SQ)* ASD 3487 (9/78, *UK4*);
  HMV TC-ASD 3487 (*C*); *EMI Int.* 063-06631Q (*E/C4*)

Sinfonietta No. 3, op. 81 (**116**)
BBC Concert Orchestra/Malcolm Arnold, *NSA* Tape M.1013W (10/10/67)
Bournemouth Sinfonietta/Ronald Thomas, *HMV* ASD 3868, st (7/80, *UK4*);
  HMV TC-ASD 3868 (*C*); *EMI Int.* 063-07290, st (*E/C4*)

Sky West and Crooked (**276**)
Film available on Rank Video Library cassette.
Title song – The Wayfarers: *Decca* F.12339 (4/66, *UK5*); *Decca* DFE 8655 (*UK5*)

Solomon and Sheba (**261**)
Soundtrack: Orchestra/conductor (?), *United Artists* UAL 4051/UAS 5051,
  st (*USA4*); (Fr.) *United Artists* UASF 5061, st (*E/C4*)
Exc only: (R) *United Artists* UAL 3122/UAS 6122, st (*USA4*)

Sonata for Flute and Piano, op. 121 (**161**)
Judith Pearce/Ian Brown (Nash Ensemble), *Hyperion* A66173 (5/86, *UK4*)

Sonata for Viola and Piano, op. 17 (**30**)
Roger Chase/Ian Brown (Nash Ensemble), *Hyperion* A66171 (5/86, *UK4*)

Sonata No. 1 for Violin and Piano, op. 15 (**28**)
Marcia Crayford/Ian Brown (Nash Ensemble), *Hyperion* A66171 (5/86, *UK4*)

Sonata No. 2 for Violin and Piano, op. 43 (**62**)
Marcia Crayford/Ian Brown (Nash Ensemble), *Hyperion* A66171 (5/86, *UK4*)

Sonatina for Clarinet and Piano, op. 29 (**45**)
Keith Pearson/Julian Dawson, *NSA* Tape M 372W (10/5/65)
Jack Brymer/David Lloyd, *Discourses* ABK 16, st (7/74, *UK4*)
James Campbell/James York, *Crystal* 333, st (2/79, *USA4*)
Mark Walton/Paul Bateman, *Chalumeau* EBY 001, st (7/81, *UK4*); *NSA* Tape
  M 7977BW (25/4/79)
Christopher Allen/Lynda Chang, *NSA* Tape T2346W (4/7/79)
Guy Dangain/Jens Harold Bratlie, *Simax* PS 1016, st (2/83, *E/C4*)
Lynn Holman/Graeme Humphrey, *Bedivere* BVR 311, st (6/83, *E/C4*)
Michael Collins/Ian Brown (Nash Ensemble), *Hyperion* A66172 (5/86, *UK4*)

Sonatina for Flute and Piano, op. 19 (**32**)
Judith Pearce/Ian Brown (Nash Ensemble), *Hyperion* A66172 (5/86, *UK4*)

Sonatina for Oboe and Piano, op. 28 (**43**)
Vladimir Kurlin/M. Karandashova, *Melodiya* D.026527/8 (1970, *USSR4*)
David Cowsill/Marigold Pickerill, *NSA* Tape M 4853W (14/2/73)

Senia Trubashnik/Lara Trubashnik, *Pavane* ADW 7007, st (5/80, *E/C4*)
Finale (arr Vera Gray): Ensemble/Vera Gray, *HMV* CLP 3762 (10/74, *UK4*)
Gareth Hulse/Ian Brown (Nash Ensemble), *Hyperion* A66172 (5/86, *UK4*)

Sonatina for Recorder and Piano, op. 41 (**57**) [version for flute and piano]
Judith Pearce/Ian Brown (Nash Ensemble), *Hyperion* A66172 (5/86, *UK4*)

Song of Freedom, op. 109 (**146**)
Harrow Schools' Girls Choir/City of London Brass Band/Geoffrey Brand, *Decca*
    SB 313, st (9/74, *UK4*)

Song of Simeon, op. 67 (**97**)
Ambrosian Singers/English Chamber Orchestra/Malcolm Arnold, *BBC(SA)*
    30763 (12/1/67); *BBC(TD)* 119212

The Sound Barrier, op. 38 (**54**)
Orchestra and conductor not named, 'Recorded Productions' Acetate (24/3/53,
    P)
Royal Philharmonic Orchestra/Malcolm Arnold, *Columbia* SED 5542 (12/57,
    UK5); (R) *Ariel* CBF 13 (*USA4*)

String Quartet No. 2, op. 118 (**157**)
Allegri Quartet, *BBC(TD)* 139467/8

Symphony for Brass Instruments, op. 123 (**163**)
Philip Jones Brass Ensemble/Howard Snell, *NSA* Tape T 2578 BW (20/10/79);
    Argo ZRG 906, st (11/79, *UK4*); *Argo* KZRC 906 (*C*)

Symphony for Strings, op. 13 (**26**)
Welbeck Symphony Orchestra/Maurice Miles, Acetate (no date, *P*); *NSA* Tape
    T. 5516W

Symphony No. 1, op. 22 (**36**)
Bournemouth Symphony Orchestra/Malcolm Arnold, *HMV* ASD 3823,
    st (6/80, *UK4*); *HMV* TC-ASD 3823 (*C*); *EMI Int.* 063-07174, st (*E/C4*)

Symphony No. 2, op. 40 (**56**)
BBC Scottish Orchestra/Alexander Gibson, Acetate (9/2/54, *P*)
Royal Philharmonic Orchestra/Malcolm Arnold, *Philips* NBL 5021 (12/55,
    UK4); *Epic* LC 3422 (5/58, *USA4*); *Philips Int.* N.10712L (*E/C4*)
BBC Northern Symphony Orchestra/Malcolm Arnold, *BBC(SA)* Tape MT
    33410 (26/9/69)
Bournemouth Symphony Orchestra/Sir Charles Groves, *Musical Heritage Society*

MHS 4766Z (*USA4*); *HMV(SQ)* ASD 3353 (6/77, *UK4*); *HMV* TC-ASD
3353 (*C*); *EMI Int.* 063-06383Q, st (*E/C4*); (R) *HMV Greensleeve* ED 29 0461
1, st (9/85, *UK4*); *HMV Greensleeve* ED 29 0461 4 (*C*)
London Symphony Orchestra/George Hurst, *BBC(TD)* 28.02

Symphony No. 3, op. 63 (**85**)
London Philharmonic Orchestra/Malcolm Arnold, *Everest* LPBR 6021/SDBR
3021, st (7/59, *USA4*); (R) *World Record Club* T.99/ST.99, st (1/62, *UK4*);
(R) *Everest* SDBR 3021, st (1/69, *UK4*); (R) *Desto* DC 6448, st (9/78, *USA4*)

Symphony No. 4, op. 71 (**100**)
BBC Symphony Orchestra/Malcolm Arnold, *BBC(SA)* 26502/3 (11/11/60);
BBC(SA) Tape T.31653 (11/11/60); *BBC(TD)* 121102/3; *NSA* Tape P.256W
(2/11/60)
Lisbon Conservatoire Orchestra/Peter Michaels, *Aries* LP 1622, st (pirate
recording of above, *USA4*)

Symphony No. 5, op. 74 (**104**)
BBC Scottish Orchestra/Malcolm Arnold, *NSA* Tape P 726R (23/10/71)
City of Birmingham Symphony Orchestra/Malcolm Arnold, *HMV* ASD 2878,
st (5/73, *UK4*); *HMV* TC-ASD 2878 (*C*); *EMI Int.* 063-05266 (*E/C4*);
(R) *HMV Greensleeve* ED 29 0461 1, st (9/85, *UK4*); *HMV Greensleeve*
ED 29 0461 4 (*C*)

Symphony No. 6, op. 95 (**128**)
BBC Northern Symphony Orchestra/Malcolm Arnold, *BBC(SA)* T.32077
(28/6/68); *BBC(TD)* 130424; *NSA* Tape 1165R

Symphony No. 8, op. 124 (**164**)
BBC Northern Symphony Orchestra/Sir Charles Groves, *NSA* Tape 5399BW
(2/10/81)

Tam O'Shanter, op. 51 (**70**)
Royal Philharmonic Orchestra/Malcolm Arnold, 'Recorded Productions'
Acetate (16/8/55, *P*)
Royal Philharmonic Orchestra/John Hollingsworth, *Philips* NBL 5021 (12/55,
UK4); *Philips* NBE 11038 (9/56, *UK5*); *Epic* LC 3422 (5/58, *USA4*); *Philips*
SBF 117, st (11/59, *UK5*); *Philips Int.* N.10712L (*E/C4*)
Philharmonia Orchestra/Malcolm Arnold, *Columbia* SED 5529 (2/56, *UK5*)
New Symphony Orchestra/Alexander Gibson, *Victor* LM 2225/LSC 2225,
st (2/59, *USA4*); *RCA* SB 2020, st (4/59, *UK4*); *RCA* RB 16156 (9/59, *UK4*);
(R) *Decca* SPA 175, st (1/72, *UK4* and *E/C4*); (R) *Decca* (set) 6.48 172 DM
(*E/C4*); *Decca* (set) 4.48 172 OM (*C*)

Royal Philharmonic Orchestra/Bernard Keeffe, *BBC(SA)* Tape T 38897
  (10/3/79); *NSA* Tape P 1474/5 BW
Scottish National Orchestra/Sir Alexander Gibson, *Chandos (D)* ABRD 1032,
  st (11/81, *UK4*); *Chandos* ABTD 1032 (*C*); (R) *Chandos(D)* CBRD 1008
  (10/82, *UK4*); (R) *Chandos* CBTD 1008 (*C*); (R) *Chandos* CHAN 8301 CD
  (7/83, *UK*)

Three Shanties for Wind Quintet, op. 4 (**16**)
London Wind Quintet, *NSA* Tape M. 238R (20/7/63); *Argo* RG 326/ZRG 5326,
  st (2/63, *UK4*); *London Argo* RG 326/ZRG 5326, st (8/64, *USA4*); (R) *Decca*
  SPA 396, st (8/75, *UK4*); (R) *Decca* KCSP 396 (*C*)
Students of the Royal College of Music, *BBC(SA)* 31960 (27/6/68)
Paris Wind Ensemble, *Vega* C 35 A 140 (*E/C3*)
Leningrad Philharmonic Wind Ensemble, *Melodiya* D. 018713/4 (*USSR4*);
  Melodiya SM. 02249/50, st (*USSR4*)
Estonian Philharmonic Wind Ensemble, *Melodiya* D. 22951/2 (*USSR3*)
Frosunda-Bläser Quintet, *BIS* LP-136, st (3/80, *E/C4*)
Barry Tuckwell Wind Quintet, *EMI Australia* OASD 7612, st (*E/C4*); *Nonesuch*
  78022-1, st (5/84, *USA4*)
Harlan Green Players, *CBC* SM 253, st (*E/C4*)
Belgian Woodwind Quintet, *Pavane* ADW 7152, st (8/84, *E/C4*)
Judith Pearce/Gareth Hulse/Michael Collins/John Pigneguy/Brian Wightman
  (Nash Ensemble), *Hyperion* A66173 (5/86, *UK4*)
No. 1 only: Trinity College of Music Wind Band, *BBC(SA)* Tape MT.31946
  (8/11/67)
No. 3 only: Francis Chagrin Ensemble/Francis Chagrin, *BBC(TD)* 378.02

Tiger in the Smoke (**250**)
Excs only: *Rank* F.M. (No.?) (*UK2*); *BBC(SA)* 2307 (1956)

To Youth (**23**)
Abridged version: National Youth Orchestra/Reginald Jacques, *BBC(SA)*
  11703/4 (21/4/48)

Toy Symphony, op. 62 (**84**)
BBC Concert Orchestra/Rae Jenkins, *NSA* Tape P9W2 (14/12/63)

Trapeze (**246**)
Soundtrack: Orchestra/Muir Mathieson, *Columbia* CL 870 (4/57, *USA4*)
Soundtrack excs: Lola's Theme/Mike and Lola's Love Theme: Orchestra/Muir
  Mathieson, *Philips* PB 626 (9/56, *UK1*)
Other exc: Lola's Theme: Steve Allen and his Orchestra, *Vogue* Q 72184 (8/56,
  UK1); *Vogue* 45-72184 (*UK5*)

Trio for Flute, Viola and Bassoon, op. 6 (**18**)
William Bennett (fl)/Kenneth Essex (va)/Gwydion Brooke (bsn), *NSA* Tape
    066W (10/1/65)
Judith Pearce/Roger Chase/Brian Wightman (Nash Ensemble), *Hyperion* A66172
    (5/86, *UK4*)

Tunes of Glory (**264**)
Soundtrack: Orchestra/Malcolm Arnold, *United Artists* UAL 4086/UAS 5086, st
    (*USA4*)
Theme: Cambridge Strings, *London* LL 3238/PS 231, st (*USA4*); *Decca* F.11303
    (2/61, *UK5*)
Excs: Frank Cordell and his Orchestra, *HMV Pop* 824 (3/61, *UK5*)
Mitch Miller Group, *Philips* PB 1107 (4/61, *UK1*)
Other excs (not identified): *London* LL 3247/PS 237, st (*USA4*); *Phase Four* SP
    44020, st (*USA4*); *Mercury* MG 20688/ST 60688, st (*USA4*)

Two Ceremonial Psalms for Treble Voices, op. 35 (**51**)
No. 1 only: Ryesingers Choir/Leslie Brownbill, *MSR* MSRS 1429, st (*c.*78/9,
    UK4)

Two John Donne Songs, op. 114 (**152**)
Ian Partridge (t)/Jennifer Partridge (pno), *NSA* Tape M.7267BW (20/10/77)

United Nations (**90**)
Band of the Royal Military School of Music/Morley College Symphony
    Orchestra/Malcolm Arnold, *Angel* 35800 (*USA4*); *Columbia* 33CX 1617 (1/59,
    UK4); (R) *World Record Club* T.701/ST.701, st (8/68, *UK4*); (R) *HMV* (set)
    SLS 870(3) (3/75, *UK4*);(R) *HMV* (set) SLS 5069(3) (11/76, *UK4*); (R) *EMI Int.*
    (set) 153 – 52125/7 (*E/C4*)

Variations on a Ukrainian Folk Song, op. 9 (**21**)
Edna Iles, *NSA* Tape 2995R (9/77)

Whistle Down the Wind (**267**)
Film available on Rank Video Library cassette 0053C
Theme music: The Wayfarers (instrumental), *Decca* F.11370 (7/62, *UK5*)
The Bachelors (vocal and instrumental) with orchestra, *Decca* LK 4721/ SKL
    4721, st (9/65, *UK4*)
Bill McGuffie Quartet, *Philips* SBL 7854, st (2/69, *UK4*)
Theme (arr Paul Fenoulhet): Midland Radio Orchestra/Norrie Paramor, *BBC*
    REB 204, st (1975, *UK4*); (R) *BBC* RED 226, st (3/76, *UK4*)
Theme (arr Ed Welch): Rank Concert Orchestra/Ed Welch, *United Artists* UAG
    30281, st (5/80, *UK4*).

Exc: – We Three Kings (March arr Malcolm Arnold): Johnny Keating and the Z
  Men, *Piccadilly* NEP 34011 (12/62, *UK5*)

The Wildcats of St Trinian's (**283**)
Film available on Enterprise Home video cassette, 016

Women in Our Time (**177**)
Excs: (1) Machines, (2) Montage – Peace and War: London Symphony
  Orchestra/Muir Mathieson, *Rank* F.M.37 (*UK2*); *BBC(SA)* 12827 (18/2/49)

SELECT LIST OF WORKS BY OTHER COMPOSERS CONDUCTED BY ARNOLD

Auber: *Overture: Le Cheval de Bronze*, BBC Northern Orchestra, *NSA* Tape
  M169W (21/3/63)
Berlioz: *Romeo and Juliet* (excs), BBC Northern Symphony Orchestra, *NSA*
  Tape P84 (11/10/64)
Bliss: Concerto for Two Pianos/Jacob: Concerto for Three Hands, Cyril Smith
  and Phyllis Sellick/City of Birmingham Symphony Orchestra, *HMV* ASD
  2612, st (10/70, *UK4*); (R) *HMV Greensleeve* ESD 7065, st (11/78, *UK4*); (R)
  HMV Greensleeve TC-ESD 7065 (2/79, *C*)
Brahms: Symphony No. 3, BBC Northern Symphony Orchestra, *NSA* Tape
  P84 (11/10/64)
John Gardner: Symphony No. 1, BBC Northern Symphony Orchestra, *NSA*
  Tape P238 (7/8/67)
Liszt: *Mazeppa*, BBC Northern Orchestra, *NSA* Tape 058W (21/3/63)
John Lord: Concerto for Group and Orchestra,★ Deep Purple/Royal
  Philharmonic Orchestra, *Harvest/EMI* – SHVL 767, st (*UK4*); *Harvest/EMI*
  TC-SHVL 767 (*C*). Film available on BBC Video
John Lord: *Gemini Suite*,★ Soloists/London Symphony Orchestra, *Purple/EMI* –
  TPSA 7501, st (1971, *UK4*)
Thomas Merritt: Coronation March arr (**307**)/Thomas Merritt: Anthems and
  Carols arr (**308**), Choirs/St Dennis Silver Band/St Agnes Silver Band, *Hassell*
  HASLP 938/9, (*UK3*)
Mozart: Symphony No. 25 in G Minor (K. 183), BBC Northern Orchestra,
  NSA Tape M171W (21/3/63)
Rossini: *Overture: The Italian Girl in Algiers*, BBC Northern Symphony
  Orchestra, *NSA* Tape P84 (11/10/64)
Rubbra: *Motet: Veni Creator Spiritus*, op. 130, BBC Chorus/London
  Philharmonic Orchestra, *NSA* Tape M865R (5/8/66)
Rubbra: Symphony No. 3, BBC Northern Symphony Orchestra, *NSA* Tape
  P247W (25/9/67)

William Walton/Ron Goodwin: Film soundtrack – *The Battle of Britain* (see **281**), Orchestra, *United Artists* UAS 5201, st (1/70, *USA4*); *United Artists* UAS 29019, st (9/69, *UK4*); (R) *Sunset* SLS 50407, st (10/77, *UK4*); (R) *Sunset* TC-50407 (*C*)

*Two periodical articles are of interest in relation to the two John Lord recordings: Richard Robson: 'Successful mix of pop and classics', *Records Retailer*, 4 October 1969, and Michael Chanan: 'Concerto for Deep Purple', *Music and Musicians*, December 1969.

INDEX OF ARNOLD'S WORKS

GENERAL INDEX